Geo Annand.
2208 N Harrison St
Wilmington
Del.

ROAMIN' IN THE GLOAMIN'

SIR HARRY LAUDER

ROAMIN' IN THE GLOAMIN'

BY

SIR HARRY LAUDER

AUTHOR OF
"A MINSTREL IN FRANCE"

WITH 29 ILLUSTRATIONS

PHILADELPHIA & LONDON
J. B. LIPPINCOTT COMPANY
1928

Dedicated
to the
Memory
of
Nance
and
John

to whom there are many
references in these pages

TO MY FRIENDS ALL OVER THE WORLD

MY PUBLISHERS tell me that I must write a Foreword to this book of my life. As I have put everything into the volume that I think is worth telling about myself, my forty years in the glare of the footlights, and my experiences in many lands, I am at some loss just what to say here. Yet there are one or two observations which I feel I must make even if they strike, for me at least, a very sad note. I had more than half-finished "Roamin' In The Gloamin'" when my dear wife was suddenly taken from me. The blow left me prostrate for many weeks; I was like a man "in a dwam," as we say in Scotland. Nance had meant so much to me. She was not only my wife—she was my inspiration and my guiding star. She had as much to do with my success as I had myself. She was my constant and loving companion on more than half a million miles of world wanderings. She was proud of me and I worshipped her.

A month or two after she was laid to rest in the Highland glen near our old home in Argyllshire I remembered that she had been looking forward very much to the publication of this book and I determined to go ahead and do my best to finish it. This task gradually brought me back to something like an even keel. But I simply could not bring myself to make any reference to Lady Lauder's death; I continued the book in the same strain as I had started it and wrote as if she were still with me, watching over, guiding, and encouraging me. Otherwise I do not think I could ever have completed this story of my life. For she was—and still is—part and parcel of it.

Another thing I would like to say is that I have been blessed with some great friendships. I do not think I have ever been what is called an "easy man to get on with." In

7

my heart of hearts I am really very shy, perhaps a bit quick in the temper, perhaps, also, too much inclined to "keep myself to myself"—in other words, slow to make friends and rather a difficult man to understand. It is all the greater joy to me, therefore, to know that I have succeeded in winning the sincere affection of many good fellows at home, in America, and in the dominions over the seas. Several of these I must mention by name.

If there is another such as Tom Vallance anywhere else in the world the man who claims him as manager, secretary, valet, and interesting companion over a period of thirty-five years is indeed a lucky person! You, Tom, have been a partner in Harry Lauder, Limited (strictly limited!) all these years! You have travelled to the ends of the earth with me and have never once missed a train or a steamer or been late for an "entrance." You are as faithful and loyal to me as your dear sister Nance was, and I can say no more than that. Without you I would be like a fish out of water. And you've had a lot to put up with, mind I'm tellin' you! When, if ever, you throw your hand in, Tom, I'll just creep awa' to ma bed and die!

Will Morris! The greatest, the straightest, and the gamest Jew I have ever met. For twenty years we have worked together in America, Will, and I never knew you do a mean or a petty action. I'll tell the world that your word is ten times better than your bond! No contracts in writing are necessary after Will Morris blinks his eyes and says, "Yep, I agree!" I suppose, my dear Will, you have made far more money out of me than I have out of you but we'll cry quits with the remark that if you had a gold mine to work in Harry Lauder he had a veritable Bonanza in his American manager.

And "Ted" Carroll. The man who "put me over" in Australia, South Africa, and in a hundred cities "east of Suez." The gentlest creature in trousers I have ever met—

genuine to the core and shrewd with an exceeding great shrewdness in all stage business and theatrical ventures. The name of E. J. Carroll is honoured all over the world among men who appreciate simplicity of bearing, level dealing, and high personal character. He has a very secure corner in the heart of Harry Lauder.

If I have mentioned these three men first it is because they have been intimately associated with my professional career over a long period of years and because I have been in close touch with them continually. But there are other friendships of an intimate and personal nature which I have come to value even more highly since Fate robbed me first of my son and then my wife. My brother Alec and his family have meant more to me of late than I can find words to express. Greta, his daughter, has joined the little household at Dunoon, and only her sweet presence makes Laudervale —place of delightful ghosts and fragrant memories—still habitable for her lonely old uncle.

Then there is Donald Munro, that brawny son of Deeside whom I have loved as a brother for over thirty years, who fishes with me, golfs with me, and rambles over the heather with me, whose wife knits me socks and woollies and scarves and neither counts trouble nor cost if it is for her one-time brother artiste of the concert platform. May Donald and his wife live for ever! And may he still be Provost of Banchory when it absorbs the neighbouring town of Aberdeen!

Other names which may mean comparatively little to most people but which stand ace-high with me are those of "Wullie" Thomson of Glasgow, Col. Duncan F. Neill Keills of Argyllshire—the man who has sailed Sir Thomas Lipton's yachts for years and knows more about big yachting than any amateur in the world—"Bob" Thomson of Peckham, whose daughter Mildred would have been my son's wife had the war not claimed him a willing victim, "Willie"

Cochrane of Manchester, Duncan MacDonald of Invercargill, New Zealand, and that wonderful pair of Caledonian enthusiasts in New York, Colonel Walter Scott, head of Butler Brothers in Broadway, and Duncan McInnes, who occupies a trustworthy position under the municipality of that great city.

I have left my very dear old friend and chum, William Blackwood, to the last because somehow I always feel that he is in a special class all by himself. He has been chief of my unpaid personal staff for more than twenty years; he and his wife have been the kindest of hosts to me and mine since ever they set up house together. Blackwood knows every detail of my life and career—in fact he knows so much about me that the following pages are full of stories and incidents which I would never have written had he not recalled them to my memory and urged that they were worth the telling. Indeed, I am free to confess that without his expert and gladly given services over many months this volume might never have been written at all!

HARRY LAUDER

CONTENTS

CONTENTS

CONTENTS

CONTENTS

ILLUSTRATIONS

ILLUSTRATIONS

ROAMIN' IN THE GLOAMIN'

CHAPTER ONE

WEE HARRY

"WHEN are you going to retire, Harry?"

That people all over the world should persist in asking this question of a young and strong fellow only anxious to get on with his job of work and save a shilling or two for his old age annoys me very much! I don't know how this rumour about my retiral got abroad but if I knew who started it I would have something serious to say to him. It's not fair to a youthful comedian with a future before him and anxious to earn an honest but precarious living!

Only a few months ago when I was stepping on the gangway of the Berengaria at New York for one of my occasional visits home from the country that has been so good to me during the past twenty years a man edged his way through the crowd at the dock, seized me by the hand, and started to wring it like a pump-handle.

"Good-bye, Sir Harry," he exclaimed, "Good-bye and God bless you! My grandfather was one of your greatest admirers and so was my father. I've heard you myself all over the States and would have liked my boys to see and hear you. But that'll never be now, I suppose. Good-bye, good-bye!"

I felt bewildered. I was stunned. I was tongue-tackit, as we say in Scotland. Not so much by the evident emotion of the fellow's farewell, but by a dawning realization of the fact that I have come to be regarded as the Methuselah of the theatrical artistes of the world. What I ought to have done was to bend my hoary old back, stagger up the gangway with "mony a cough an' clocher," and wave a palsied hand in a long, last adieu to the American people. Actually

19

I dashed up the steps, two at a time, took up a good position at the rail and started to yell to my old crony, Colonel Walter Scott, "Here's tae us, Wattie! Wha's like us? Deil a yin!! See ye again next year!"

Me retire! How do the people that ask me the question know that I have made enough money to retire on? Do they not stop to think that if I retired I would have to spend a lot of money without earning any? And that such a prospect, if all the tales about Harry Lauder be true, would be altogether too dreadful for him to contemplate?

I will go the length of admitting that I have been seriously considering the cutting down of my annual farewell tours! These have been going on for quite a number of years now but the people at home and in America and Australia and South Africa and New Zealand continue to give me so much encouragement—and this is one of those words that can be written either in letters or figures!—that I sometimes think I will just carry on "to the end of the road." One of these days, however, I'm afraid I'll be writing a letter to Will Morris in New York, or Sir Alfred Butt in London, or the Tait Brothers in Melbourne, or dear old Ted Carroll anywhere, saying that I won't be leaving Dunoon and the heather hills o' Scotland for any more professional engagements. Perhaps! On the other hand—perhaps not!!

Honestly why should I retire? I like my work. I am happiest when on the stage—I mean by that that my whole heart is in my job. I never tire of it. If I lie off for a few weeks, as I shall have to do occasionally now if I am to write this book of my life and wanderings, I gradually get more and more restless and the only thing that pulls me together is to know that I "open" at such-and-such a place on such-and-such a date. Never a day elapses either when I am at home or "on tour" but I spend some hours of it singing and lilting and humming and strumming. And it has been the same with me for fifty years. In the mill, in the mine, in my bed, in my bath, in the train, on the steamboat, fishing, golfing, or shooting—I seem to be singing all the time.

I think singing must be a sort of disease with me. But in my case it has been both a pleasant and profitable disease, and you can't say that about any other disease! One day I began to calculate the number of times I have sung each of my famous songs. I began, I say, but I never finished—the numbers ran into millions! An eternal spring of simple melody has welled in my head ever since I was a little fellow at my mother's knee. Even today if I suddenly get a new tune or a new twist to an old one I cannot rest until I have evolved words to fit it, and if I hit upon a phrase or a couplet or an idea which appeals to me I *must* wed the words to a tune before I lay my head on the pillow.

It is not at all unlikely, however, that the writing of my memoirs—these roamin's in the gloamin's of a crowded professional life—will drive some of the liltin' an' singin' out of my head for a month or two. A man cannot write and sing at the same time—as I am now beginning to find out—but there's nothing to prevent me throwing down my Waterman every now and then and bursting into song. In this joyous occupation I shall have the company of the larks and mavises and the "blackies" who sing all day long in my garden on the bonnie bank o' Clyde. Yes, we'll all make melody together because we love to sing, and a simple song is the finest tonic and brain-reviver in the world. When Harry Lauder can sing no more there will be no more Harry Lauder!

* * * * *

I wish all my readers could see the scene upon which I gazed with an almost holy rapture a few minutes ago. I had gone upstairs and strolled through the open window on to the balcony of Laudervale which overlooks the water. (To be perfectly frank, I was in sair need of inspiration as to

how best to begin these memoirs and thought I might get
it from still another glimpse of dear and familiar scenes.)
It is a lovely evening in early June, the close of a day so
perfectly heavenly that even on Clydeside we have only a
few such in the very best of summers. The sun is going
down in a glory of crimson and gold and the spreading
sweeps of the Firth of Clyde are bathed in the splendour of
its slow-fading beams. There is not a ripple on the waters
for the wind has died down with the turn of the tide, leaving
all the white-sailed yachts like tiny fairy ships dotted between
the Cŭmbraes and Craigendoran, and from my own bit of
foreshore to the coasts of Renfrew and Ayr opposite.

Only two moving things are in the picture—the last
boat for Glasgow drawing away from Dunoon pier with
its load of trippers, and a new red-funnelled Atlantic liner
doing her last trial run over the measured mile from the
Cloch lighthouse to Wemyss Bay. The wooded hills behind
me and their fellows rising from the picturesque bends of
the Firth to left and right are full of a silent majesty, for
the birds have gone to sleep long ago in readiness for the
early chorus with which they shall waken me tomorrow. In
the clear calm air I range my eyes up and down across the
Firth for many many miles, picking out all the delightful
landmarks I know so well. Suddenly a girl's merry laugh
from the riverside road below me breaks the enchantment
—and yet it does not, for me, break it altogether because
she and her lover are "Roamin' in the gloamin' on the bonnie banks o' Clyde." Oh, but it's a braw, braw scene; the
wide world o'er which I have wandered for twenty years
can offer me none so fair or heart-warming.

Back once more at my desk—built, by the way, like the
parquet flooring of my den, of wonderfully beautiful mahogany brought back with me from the Philippines on one
of my passing visits—I again take up the pen and wonder
where and how to begin the real story of my life. For I feel

that thus far I have been wandering about the stage looking for a spotlight in which to open my performance.

Yes, here I am, standing on the stage, ready and anxious to begin. But the visions that crowd upon my brain prevent me writing the words that will form, as my spoken words have always done hitherto, the spark of vital and immediate contact between myself and my audience. I see a very humble home in Scotland, a mere "but-and-ben" inhabited by a father and mother and seven young children of whom Harry is the eldest. A short but sturdy fellow of nine or ten years of age. The little household is never far from the line dividing poverty from penury. Father and mother are hard-working, God-fearing folks, honest, independent, but always dreading the hour when disaster and hunger may assail them and their brood of weans. I see the day when the bread-winner is suddenly cut off and the weeping wife and bairns are thrown, penniless, upon the world. I see the oldest of the boys, not yet twelve years of age, working as a half-timer in a flax mill on the east-coast of Scotland. In the evenings, he and his mother toil in the little kitchen from six o'clock till ten tearing old ropes and twine and hawsers into "tow," their four hours' labour bringing them a few much-needed coppers. Later, I see Harry go down the coal-pit in Lanarkshire as a miner's boy, and, kissing his mother good-bye on that first raw November morning, I hear him say, "Mither, Mither, dinna greet! I'll work for you and the wee yins as hard as ever I can!" And again I see the still very youthful miner winning his first prize as a comedian at a village "soiree," and I remember his dreams of a London appearance and the plaudits of the multitude— of fame! Yes, I can see in my mind's eye that first memorable night in a London music hall when the "wee Scotch comic" held up the "show" for over half an hour and became a stage celebrity in a night. The visions begin to tumble over each other now. There are so many of them;

they press themselves forward in swift and kaleidoscopic array. They carry me to "a' the airts the wind can blaw"—to all the ends of the earth. They are peopled by kings and queens and princes and presidents; by great and famous men and women, by potentates and personalities whose names are as household words wherever the English language is spoken. My head is in a whirl. Is it possible, I ask myself, that all this can actually have happened to me? Surely I must be dreaming. I'll fill my pipe and rest awhile. I feel that I must come back to earth because if I let my mind linger on these visions and these memories I am afraid I shall never get down to the mental state in which I can tell a coherent story of a life which has been full of incident, full of fun, full of amazing experiences, full of striving and planning and earning and saving, but fullest of all, of downright hard work!

I was born in Portobello, a mile or two from Edinburgh, on the fourth of August, 1870. My father, John Lauder, was a potter. He worked in a small pottery in Müsselburgh where the principal output was jelly-jars and ginger-pop bottles. His father was also John Lauder, a working carpenter, and I well remember him in my childhood's years. He was a big impressive man with a personality which he carried with a good deal of dignity. He was very proud of being a Lauder of Lauderdale, a district of the borders famous in Scottish history, song, and story. The old Lauders, so far as I have been able to make out, must have had some connection with the Bass Rock, that bluff and rocky island that stands sentinel-like at the southern side of the Firth of Forth. Because I can remember my grandfather, perhaps when he had had a glass of beer on a Saturday night, solemnly tapping his chest and telling my father, "John, I'm a Lauder of the Bass! So are you! Never forget that you are a Lauder!"

Even as a very small boy I recollect wondering what

good the gaunt and grim Bass Rock can ever have been to
the ancient Lauders. Later I discovered that it was reputed
in the old days to have been the haunt and hiding place of
a nest of villainous Scottish pirates. This thought pleased
me much; every time I looked at the weather-beaten rock I
pictured my ancestors as bold buccaneers setting forth from
their caves on the rock to harry and rob the English and
any other nation—but particularly the English. This pleasant task is still popularly supposed to be one of the principal
occupations of Scotland!

My mother was a MacLennan. She came of real Highland stock. Her full name was Isabella Urquhart MacLeod
MacLennan. Her people came from the Black Isle in Ross-
shire. She was a splendid woman in every respect and I hold
her memory in reverence. Like all Highland women she had
a great strain of romance and mysticism in her make-up.
She was full of superstition and believed implicitly in "signs
and portents." She had a never-ending fund of stories about
witches and war-locks and fairies and water-kelpies; when
her family grew more numerous I can remember us sitting
round her knee listening, wide-eyed and open-mouthed, with
many a nervous look over our shoulders, to tales of supernatural happenings on the mountains or in the glens or on
the lochs and rivers of the Black Isle. The request, "Tell us
a story, Mither!" never found her wanting. She would stop
her housework at any minute of the day to spin us young-
sters a tale of romance or chivalry or mystery or horror. I
loved her stories from my earliest years. She had all the
Scottish Clan histories at her tongue's tip and nothing delighted me more than tales of the MacLennans, the Urqu-
harts, the Logans, or the MacLeods. Thus did I become
imbued with Highland lore and romance. Today whenever
I sing "Sure, by Tummel and Loch Rannoch and Lochaber
I will go," my blood boils in a sort of "Hielan' ecstasy"

compared with which there is no other similar emotion in the world.

I don't remember the "flittin'" from Portobello to Müsselburgh where we moved so as to be nearer the pottery where my father was employed. But I do remember that the family circle seemed to grow very rapidly. Every year another "wean" appeared on the scene. Almost as soon as I was able to walk I began to act as a sort of infant nurse to the others and this continued all through my early boyhood. For many hours I was wrapped in a "plaid" which not only contained me but a wee brother or sister unable to walk—I was a sort of gypsy mother with an infant strapped to me. My parents used to say that Wee Harry was as good as any professional nurse. That's as it may be, but all my life I have been very fond of children. All my brothers and sisters grew up to manhood and womanhood, and, with the exception of George, who died some years ago at Dunoon, they are alive and kicking in different parts of the world. Matt is in California. He has three sons who all fought in the war and got back safe and sound. Jock is in Newcastle, New South Wales, while Alec has settled down as a business man in Hamilton after several years on the stage. Bella, Jean, and Mary are all married and are still living in "the West." I see them from time to time and many's the happy hour we spend together recalling the old days.

When I was about five years of age I was sent to a little school not far from the pottery where my father worked. My recollections of the "penny bookie"—the first primer of every Scottish child—are rather hazy. But I do remember that the teacher was another Highlander, named Fraser, and that he was rather a fearsome man with a stubby, sandy beard. In these days there was no kindergarten nonsense about the cheaper Scottish schools. The dominies focussed on what was known as the essentials—the three R's—reading, 'riting, and 'rithmetic.

That I was either a bright or a promising pupil I cannot assert, in fact I think I must have been rather a dull boy to begin with because the only thing that really interested me was the daily lesson in Scottish history. Mr. Fraser was one of those perfervid Scots—and they still exist—who evidently thought that there was only one country and one nation in the world, his own. The history lesson was not so much an inculcation of dates and facts about the happenings in the world as a laudation and glorification of all things Scottish, its kings, its national heroes, its poets, its soldiers and its ministers. Wallace and Bruce, Rabbie Burns, Walter Scott and David Livingstone all came automatically into the daily "oration"; we boys were urged to revere and worship their names as the noblest and most wonderful men that had ever been born. The geography lesson was pretty much on the same lines. We learned all about the Scottish counties and cities, the mountains and streams, the bens and the glens of our native land. Scotland was the best and the bonniest place in the whole world; indeed no other country mattered a groat!

I may be doing an injustice to the memory of Dominie Fraser in drawing this picture of his scholastic methods, but these are the impressions he left upon my youthful mind. I can remember as well as if it had been yesterday sitting at the little narrow desk, looking up at our teacher with staring, fascinated eyes and thinking how fortunate I was to be born a Scot and not an English boy, or an Irish, or a German, or a Hottentot.

Whatever fault may be found with Fraser's method of teaching the young idea how to shoot there can be no doubt that one, at least, of his pupils became fired with a devouring passion and patriotism for his native land. There was one English boy in the school and I remember him one afternoon, as we were trooping out to the playground, saying something derogatory about Scotland and the teacher's

constant references to it as the greatest country in the world.
"England's a far better place!" he concluded. For a few seconds I was too stricken with anger to do or say anything,
but then I leaped at him like a wild cat. He was bigger and
older than me and I got the worst of the argument, but as
I wandered down the lane nursing my injuries I felt within
me a throbbing of pride that I had been able to strike my
first blow for the country I adored.

Fifty years have gone by since then. The flame of love
for "Scotland's name and Scotland's fame" still burns as
fiercely in my breast.

There is a great bit of the natural "fechter" in every
Scot and when this tendency is fanned by native song or the
skirl of the bagpipes he begins to hold up his head and cast
his eye round for any trouble there may be around requir-
ing settlement. It doesn't matter very much if it is his own
affair or not—sing "Annie Laurie" and he'll greet, whistle
"The Campbells Are Comin' " and he'll throw out his chest,
let him hear the pipers play "Up Wi' The Bonnets" and he'll
search out at once for the nearest recruiting office if there
happens to be a little war on anywhere! The emotion roused
in the heart of a Scot under either or all of these circumstances has reacted in the same way for centuries. It inspired
the victors of Bannockburn; the Scots who marched to the
relief of Lucknow; it made the Fifty-first Division (The
Highland Brigade) the most dreaded Division by the enemy
on the Western front and inspired the Kaiser to issue a special "hymn of hate" against the lads who were proud to wear
the tartans of that immortal Division.

CHAPTER TWO

BOYHOOD'S YEARS SLIP AWA'

THE story of how I came to be christened Henry will draw a smile to the faces of many Scottish people who remember how serious a matter was the naming of the children in a Scottish household up till within the past few years. Indeed, it still is, in many districts, the immemorial custom for the oldest boy of a family to be called after his father's father. Only exceedingly sound reasons must prevail for any departure from this rule. I have known family relationships to be split asunder for ever because the parents of the infant refused to be bound by tradition and bestowed on him some fancy "handle."

It was the grandfather's honour and privilege to have the "namin' o' the wean." Correspondingly, if the child was a girl the grandmother on the mother's side exercised her right. The more or less rigid adherence to this cast-iron rule, of course, had its drawbacks. You would often find six or eight or ten Johnnies, or Jamies, or Sandies of the same surname in the same village. This applied also to the Maggies or Marys or Leebs or Jeans. In my own family circles, the Lauders and the Vallances, there are so many of the same name that I have often to work out just who is referred to when any one of them is mentioned in conversation. My own opinion is that the system is all wrong. It leads to hopeless confusion.

Nowadays parents are not so stupid, and grandparents less touchy. But I would most certainly have been christened John Lauder had it not been for the fact that my father had had a bit of a "tirravee" (dispute) with his father shortly before I was born. So in revenge he insisted that I should be

called after my mother's father, Henry MacLennan. Old
Henry died in our house. He had lived with his married
daughter for some years, being very frail and unable to
work. He was a typical old Highlander in looks, speech, and
general behaviour. I remember him sitting at the ingle-neuk
reading his Gaelic Bible and telling me to be a "goot poy
an' fear the Lord." He and my mother were thoroughly
religious people and both took a great interest in teaching
me my prayers. Almost as soon as I was able to lisp I learned
the stock prayer of every Scottish infant.

> As I lie down this night to sleep
> I pray the Lord my soul may keep
> If I should die before I wake
> I pray the Lord my soul may take.

Note how the Calvinistic element of gloom and sudden
death was instilled into the Scottish infant of fifty or sixty
years ago! Well do I remember lying in bed night after
night thinking with horror of the prospect of never wakening
up again and wondering why the Lord should want to come
to Müsselburgh and take away the soul—whatever that
meant—of a poor wee boy like me! But whatever the suit-
ability of the prayers and the religion of these days to the
very tender minds of youth there can be no doubt that they
implanted themselves deeply on the mind. I am not at all
ashamed to confess that I still repeat each night the little
prayer I learned at my mother's knee.

On Sundays no work was done in our house. The food for
that day was cooked overnight. The blinds were "drawn."
The "auld folk" went to church and, when I was old enough,
I was sent to Sunday School. In the evening my mother
gathered us round and told us a story about the Covenanters
or David Livingstone or read a tale from the Old Testament.
Yes, Sunday was "the Lord's Day" in very truth. But tomorrow would be Monday!

At this stage of my early memories my mind goes back

to the first money I ever earned. You see how the Adam in
Harry Lauder asserts itself. If I am ever stumped for a story
or a subject in this book I can always turn on the money-
making tap. It will never fail me. Perhaps this is only to be
expected in the life story of a man who is supposed to think
more of "siller" than the average Scotsman and who is popularly reputed to have collected—and kept—more than his
fair share of it all over the world! But, in the meantime,
we'll "let that flea stick to the wa'!" It has been a grand
advertisement for me all my life and why should I complain
of the best free advertisement any public man ever had
anywhere, at any time?

I would be about eight years of age when a well-known
worthy in the village called Wattie Sandilands gave me the
opportunity of earning my first few coppers. He kept a large
number of pigs. The "soo craes" at Wattie's place had a
peculiar fascination for me and many an hour I spent watching their inmates. One day the old man said that if I would
help him to feed the pigs he would give me sixpence a week.
Would I? I could scarcely answer him for the thumping of
my heart. Sixpence a week for doing a job which I would
gladly have done for nothing! So the bargain was struck.
Each night for a fortnight I slipped along to Wattie's, helped
him to unload the refuse from the tins in which he collected
it all over the town, mix it and dump it in the troughs. For
two Saturdays I got my sixpence and proudly took it home
to my mother. She was not exactly enamoured of my first
job, not because of its humble nature, but owing to the fact
that Wattie had the reputation of being a very short-tem-
pered man and quick with his hands. My father, when consulted, only laughed and said that if I was feeding pigs I
was being kept out of mischief in other directions. "Besides,"
he added, "Harry may be a farmer some day and the experience will do him good." (The words were prophetic. I *was* a
farmer many years afterwards but any experience I had as

an assistant pig-feeder did not prevent me making a colossal failure of the business.) Alas, my weekly sixpence did not continue after the fortnight for one of Wattie's pigs choked itself to death through trying to eat a piece of hard dumpling which had been thrown away by some housewife. Probably it was the first she had ever made. In any case, the pig died and old man Sandilands blamed me for letting the pig eat it in the first instance and for not immediately acting as veterinary surgeon when I saw that it was in difficulties. I was sacked on the spot. To add to the injustice I was unable to sit down with any degree of comfort for a week or ten days.

My next job was to help a market gardener pick strawberries. The chief qualification for this job was the ability to whistle. No boys were engaged that couldn't whistle. They were supposed to whistle all the time they were picking the strawberries and the gardener walked round the beds watching and listening. The boy who was working alongside me was an expert whistler. In fact he whistled so loud that occasionally I left off—and had a good feed of strawberries. The pay was fourpence a day. I managed to get away with two days' pay, but on the third I fell into a trap laid by the gardener. He had evidently been suspicious of my honesty because he creeped down the side of my strawberry bed and pounced out on me when I was "gobbling" the best and biggest of the berries and making a hopeless attempt to whistle at the same time. Once more the parting between employer and employed was of a painful nature. I have never liked strawberries from that day to this. They make me feel ill whenever I see them on the fruit-stall or on the table.

In between these various—and vicarious—jobs, I was a caddie on Mǔsselburgh Links, at that time the great golfing resort of the Edinburgh gentry. We boys used to meet the golfers at the train and bombard them with requests to be allowed to "cairry yer clubs, sir, balls an' all, sir!" Although I was very small I could generally do my fair share of shouting and elbowing at the station and I got my "cairries" with the best of them.

There were no caddie-masters in those days. The contract was a simple one between golfer and boy, the price twopence a round. An understanding ruled, however, that if the caddie did his work faithfully and well and lost no balls he got an extra penny at the end of the round. Many a day I earned sixpence or ninepence as a caddie. My mother got the money as a rule, but occasionally I was tempted to spend some of my earnings in sweets or ladies' twist. This was a sort of tobacco rolled up into long oval balls and a penny worth would represent ten or twelve inches of material for all the world like a length of rough string. I do not know how I became thus early introduced to the nicotine habit. Probably I had seen the older boys buying it. In any event I learned to chew the tobacco and for years afterwards ladies' twist was always a temptation and an addiction.

The caddie-boys at Mŭsselburgh had another way of securing pocket-money. The golfers of that time had no Dunlop, or Silver King or Spalding balls to smack up the middle for two hundred and fifty yards. They played with the old gutta ball, a pill which had to be well and truly hit if the golfer's arms and spine were not to be shattered by a stone-like hitting. These guttas sometimes split in two when struck by the club. This was a joyful sight to the caddies for we were allowed to collar the pieces and put them in our pockets. At home we got hold of our mother's stew-pans and boiled the remnants of the balls until they were soft. Then the soft and "claggy" mass was rolled out on the kitchen table and shaped into whips which we sold to the miners' pony-drivers in the Carbery Coal Pits near Mŭsselburgh. When I became a miner myself a few years later I used to regret my financial transactions in this direction for the whips were vicious things and could give cruel blows to the puir wee horses working in the damp and eternal darkness of the mines.

I learned to hit a golf-ball before I was eight or nine years of age. Little did I then think that in the years to come I would myself play golf all over the world, or that my name would be associated with so many golf stories exemplifying the "nearness" of the Scottish race! Some of the best of these tales I shall tell against myself in their proper place during the course of these reminiscences. I must have a better collection of golf stories than any other golfer in the world—and most of them are true, seeing they are mostly told against myself.

Sport played quite a prominent part in my early boyhood days at Müsselburgh. My father took a keen interest in foot-racing. He had been a runner himself, but after marriage he confined his interests to training the runners of the district. Sprints, half-mile, mile, and long-distance races were tremendously popular in the midlands of Scotland about this time. Wee Johnnie Lauder had the reputation of being a peculiarly clever trainer and to get into his "stable" was considered something of an honour. He trained the winners of many races, including one Powderhall Handicap. Up till a few days ago I could not have told you the name of this victor in the historic Scottish race, but—so curiously do events work out—I have before me at this moment a letter written by an old man of seventy-one, now living in Buckie, Banffshire, telling me that he was trained by my father when he won a big Edinburgh Handicap in 1877. He signs the letter "William Young" and in it he says he has just noticed in the papers my return from America and took the notion to write me after all these years. I need quote only one sentence from Mr. Young's letter, a sentence that made a lump rise in my throat as I remembered the father whom I only knew as a little boy. "Johnnie Lauder was a straight, honest man and a thorough sportsman—what a pity he didn't live to see your success, Sir Harry!"

And so my boyhood's years slip awa'! I am not twelve

years of age, not very big, but broad and strong and as healthy as a young animal. There are seven boys and girls in the Lauder family, and I am my mother's mainstay for nursing, running messages, and generally assisting in the house. I can cook a meal, bathe a baby, and do a household washing if need be. There is great excitement one evening. My father comes home with the information that he has been offered a good situation in Pearson's Pottery at Whittington Moor, Derbyshire.

A Council of Ways and Means and Future Prospects is immediately called. The pros and cons are studied and discussed. My mother is very silent and undemonstrative all through; she does not like the idea of leaving Scotland for the "wilds of England." All her sentiments and affections are for her "ain folk" and for the land she knows and loves. I do not know it at the time, but in after years she confesses that "her heart was never in the shift." The Highland strain in her make-up foresees danger and disaster ahead; she has a premonition of impending fate. But my father is full of the bigger wages he has been offered. He thinks there will be better chances for the bairns in England. His enthusiasm wins the day. In less than a month the family packs up and we find ourselves at Whittington Moor near Chesterfield.

The few weeks we spent there seem like a dream to me now. I can only remember clearly the one big event which shattered the whole world for a poor young woman and her brood of seven children—the sudden death of my father from pneumonia. And one scene stands out, cameo-like, from the drama. It is the picture of my mother coming out, moaning, from the little room in which my father was lying. She catches me to her arms and sobs out "Oh, Harry, Harry, yer faither's deid, yer dear faither's been ta'en from us. What'll I dae, ma son, mu puir wee laddie? God help us a' in His mercy an' compassion."

There is no need to enlarge upon the scene and the grim tragedy of the whole situation. I was very, very young—not yet twelve years of age—but I did my best to comfort my weeping mother by telling her I loved her, that I would never leave her and that soon I would be able to work for her and my wee brothers and sisters. My father had been insured for £15 and this sufficed to bury him in the little churchyard at Whittington and leave a balance over, along with what the pottery people gave us, to take the family back to Scotland. My mother had relatives living in Arbroath, a little town in Forfarshire, and it is here that I again take up the story of my individual life once more.

Arbroath at that time was, and still is, a fairly prosperous township. It had quite a number of industries such as flax-mills, engineering works, tanneries, boot factories, and fishing. A good deal of shipping used the little harbour in my time, steamers of fair size landing cargoes of raw flax from Russia and the Baltic countries.

I had no difficulty in getting a job as half-timer in Gordon's Mill at the Brothick Brig. There are no half-timers in Scotland now; the law put a stop to this form of child-labour many years ago. But forty or fifty years ago it was common all over the country, particularly in the large manufacturing districts. A half-timer was so called because he put in one day at the mill and one day at the school; in other words he would toil from morning till night on Mondays, Wednesdays, and Fridays in the factory, while on Tuesdays, Thursdays, and Saturdays he would attend a school run by his employers in connection with the establishment. It may have been the other way round so far as the days of the week were concerned, but you get the idea.

Well, my task at Gordon's Mill was to be a "towie." That is, collecting the tow after it had passed through the heckling machinery and stamping it into a bag or a large tin receptacle. The "towie" had to be very careful not to

Photo. by the Scottish Photographic Touring Co., Glasgow

A FAMILY GROUP TAKEN AT TOOTING, LONDON

Mrs. Lauder (Sir Harry's Mother), Sir Harry, John Lauder, Lady Lauder, and the Famous Bulldog, Jock

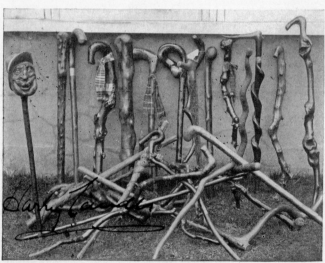

Photo. by Hayne, Tooting Broadway

A COLLECTION OF SIR HARRY'S CROOKED STICKS GATHERED FROM ALL PARTS OF THE WORLD

break the tow in its passage from the machine to the bag or
the tin. When one receptacle was filled, carefully pressed
down in coils or layers, another took its place and so the job
went on, changeless and mechanical, all day. The only relief
came by thinking that tomorrow there would be no work
to do and that school, even under such a schoolmaster as
Auld "Stumpie" Bell, was far, far better than handling an
endless film of tow from six till six.

There were perhaps fifty half-timers in Gordon's. Their
educational requirements were attended to by the said Mr.
Bell, a "character" if ever there existed one among the
dominies of Scotland. He was a little man with a shrivelled
leg so much shorter than the other than he wore an iron
standard on his boot. This certainly brought both limbs on
something like equality for length but I always thought that
the leg with the ironwork attached to it was easily the more
useful of the two! Because he used it with deadly effect
upon my anatomy more than once! My first impressions of
"Stumpie"—the nick-name was, of course, inspired by his
infirmity—were that he regarded each and every one of his
pupils as a child of Satan, choke-full of the most terrible kind
of original sin. He was the sternest disciplinarian I have
ever come across in my life. He ruled us with a rod—and a
foot!—of iron. Only the slightest provocation roused his
temper and it was God help the poor kid who came under
the storm of his wrath. He walloped the life out of us boys
day in and day out. But we loved him. He was just. He was
hard but he was fair. And he earned the respect of every
boy who passed through his drastic curriculum.

Curiously enough, his educational ideas were pretty much
on a par with those of Mr. Fraser, the Müsselburgh teacher
of whom I have already written. Not because he believed
implicitly in the "fundamentals"—the good old three R's
again—but because he was another fervent Scot to whom the
rest of the world didn't matter. Scottish history meant far

more to him than the story of the Incas in Peru or the
building up of the German Empire. And the geography of
Forfarshire, including such a fact that the Bloody Graham
of Claverhouse had his castle just outside of Dundee, was
of more vital importance than the coast-line of Japan or the
latitude of the Andaman Isles. For his own town of Arbroath he had a warm admiration. He abjured us to honour
it all our lives and never, under any circumstances, allow
anybody to say a word against it. Thus did he instil into his
pupils a sense of local patriotism in the same way as his
brother-dominie Fraser had inspired me with a sense of national pride.

There was a little public-house not far away from the
school in the Applegate. To this house of refreshment
"Stumpie" was wont occasionally to repair at the lunch hour,
and whenever any of us detected the teacher coming out
of its kindly doors we sent round the word that "Stumpie"
had had a "hauf or twa." This meant that we must all be on
our best behaviour for the rest of the day. For if the teacher
was a taskmaster when sober, he was a tyrant with a couple
of drinks in him! Woe betide any of the half-timers who
gave a wrong answer to Maister Bell under these conditions!
I have seen him work himself into a state of the most un-
governable fury, blinking his eyes, licking his teeth and lips,
snorting with rage and keeping his iron-heel constantly on
the move as if he were only waiting for a chance to bring it
into action on a pupil's shin or—well, higher up! The class
sat trembling, each boy as quiet as a mouse, until the dominie
calmed down a bit, which he always did very soon.

One day Ord's circus came to town and spread its tents
on the Common. The visit of this "mammoth combination"
—ten vans of "raging, tearing man-eaters and other beasts
of prey"—caused a sensation among the half-timers. We
held a meeting in the playground the night before and it
was decided that a committee of the boys should approach

"Stumpie" in the morning and ask for a day off to see the circus. I was one of the committee. When the morning came I, for one, rued my appointment and the other two members of the deputation did the same. You see, we knew our "Stumpie" and we had all come to the conclusion that there wasn't a thousand to one chance of him listening favourably to the request. We trooped into school and the circus was never mentioned. But at the dinner hour we held another meeting and ten or a dozen of us decided to take the bull by the horns and play truant for the rest of the day.

We had a glorious time on the Common among the circus tents. When the evening performance came along I burrowed my way underneath the canvas and had a spell-binding view of the proceedings for about half an hour. Suddenly the spell was broken by an attendant gripping me by the nape of the neck, bending me over his knee and administering severe corporal punishment with a horse brush. Then he flung me towards the canvas and ordered me to clear out the way I had come in. No snake ever wriggled quicker through the jungle than I did below the flapping canvas. Sore but satisfied, I was a hero among the other chaps for days after the circus had departed. This it did on a Sunday evening. We boys followed the cavalcade as it wound its way out of town to the north. The wooden sides of a van containing several lions were still down and naturally this was the vehicle which focussed our fascinated attention. Once, out of bravado, I dashed up close to the side of the "cage" and yelled fearsomely at the lions. One of these snarled at me and stuck an angry paw through the bars. I received such a fright that I fell, and in falling I spiked my hand against a projecting bit of iron on the wheel-rim of the next caravan. The mark is there to this day.

The sequel to our playing truant is worth telling. We had to work in the mill the following day, but next morning "Stumpie" was waiting for us in a condition of bottled-up rage. Like Tam O'Shanter's wife he had been nursing his wrath to keep it warm! I was supposed to be the bravest of the boys who had "skulked the schule," and it was decided that I should be the first of the miscreants to enter the classroom. I didn't like the job at all, but I put as good a face on it as possible and made a dash for my desk. But "Stumpie," moving with unwonted alacrity, caught me before I got there or had time to utter a word. He gave me a tremendous clout on the jaw. Fortunately, it knocked me clean underneath a desk, otherwise I would have caught a swinging kick with his iron-heel and that might have been the end of me.

The master never uttered a word. His breath was going and coming in gasps, his eyes were glaring with fury. He tried several times to voice the anger which was consuming him, but he couldn't get the words out of his mouth. After settling my "hash" he went for several of the other boys. The class was in an uproar. Two or three of the younger pupils began to cry and others, thinking that Maister Bell had gone mad, made their escape from the room and the building. I cannot imagine a scene of such a turbulent nature to have taken place in any school anywhere since education of the young began. It was an epic contest. One of the fellows upset the master's desk in the struggle, while I emerged from my place of temporary security and threw a slate which just missed Bell's head by inches. Suddenly "Stumpie" shouted out, "We'll now take the Scripture lesson!" Peace was gradually restored. And if my recollection is trustworthy the lesson that morning began with the text, "Suffer the little children to come unto me!"

Dear old "Stumpie" Bell! He had a difficult task with us half-timers, as wild and deil-may-care a bunch as you could have found in a day's march, but he left his imprint on our minds as well as on our bodies. Years after I went back to Arbroath as a "lion comique." Before going to the concert hall in the evening, I went out to hunt up my old schoolmas-

ter, but to my immense regret I learned that he had died a
year or two before. I don't mind telling you that I shed a
tear or two for his memory that evening.

My pay as a half-timer was 2/1d. per week. My mother
worked at whatever odd jobs she could get. She would
"mind" a family for a day while the parents took a holiday
or she would go out "washing" for the more prosperous
of the town's lady citizens. She was willing to do anything
at all and her geniality and determination to earn food for
her children made her a general favourite wherever she went.
I was the only member of the family old enough to do a
"hand's turn." Naturally we had a thoroughly hard time of
it but we always had something to eat. Indeed, out of my
wages I got the odd penny as pocket money. This invariably
went in tobacco; by this time I was a slave to the weed. The
"ladies' twist" did not last long. It was usually consumed
by the Sunday evening, and I had just to wait until the
week-end, or until I had picked up a penny elsewhere, before
I could satisfy my craving for more tobacco. Later, I got
taken on as one of a gang of boys to deliver the *Arbroath
Guide* on Saturday mornings. I started out as early as five
o'clock and finished up in time to go to school. For delivering probably 150 copies of the paper I earned as much as
ninepence. This meant a most substantial increase to the
family resources.

Occasionally I got my brother Matthew to assist me in
my news-vending activities. At first I thought he wanted to
do me out of my job, but I discovered that all he wanted was
to learn to smoke, like me. So I arranged that if he would
help me to deliver the papers I would teach him to smoke.
From one of the printers at the *Guide* office I got a chunk of
"thick black" one morning. This tobacco is not very well
known to smokers outside of Scotland and Ireland. It is a
peculiarly pungent brand much beloved of dock-labourers,
blacksmiths, and coal-miners—you must be a strong man to

tackle it either for chewing or smoking purposes. I had long
desire to graduate from the more or less insipid ladies'
twist to this "Man's stuff." Here was a chance to try it out.
If Matt could stand it—well, it would be all right for me. So
one Saturday afternoon I filled up a clay pipe with the thick
black, took Matt out to the Common and made him get busy
with his first smoke. In about half a minute he became violently sick, groaned and rolled his eyes, cried bitterly and
threatened to go home and tell my mother. "Matt," said I,
shaking a warning finger at my wretched brother, "if you tell
on me I'll tell on you! If you dinna say a word I'll gie ye
three brandy balls when I get my penny on Saturday!" The
brandy balls carried the day. Matt lay on the Common for
a long time and crawled home, a sick and sorry boy, about
eight o'clock at night when he knew our mother would be
out baking scones for one of the millowners' wives.

CHAPTER THREE

THIS WEAN'S GOING TO BE A SINGER

LOOKING back on these days in dear old Arbroath I think the one thing that stands out in my memory was the wonderful spirit of my dear mother. Never a word of complaint crossed her lips. She was leal to the core of her intrepid Scottish heart. How she fed us and clothed us and kept a roof over our heads I cannot imagine. But she did it. If ever there was what the Bible calls a "mother in Israel" she was one. Brave soul! Thank God she lived long enough to share in my success and spend a few years in real comfort.

I had to work hard at the mill every other day, but the days in between were glorious—after school hours! One task, and one only, I hated with all my soul. Each week my mother and I had to tease a hundred-weight of old ropes and string, ship's rigging, etc., into "tow." This stuff was sent round from one or other of the factories to the houses of the very poorest people. When teased out into yarn it was mixed up with the flax and woven into canvas or other material. The price allowed was one shilling and sixpence a hundred-weight. It took my mother and I an hour or two every night of the week, with the exception of Saturday, to reduce this dreadful stuff into tow. Both her fingers and mine were often bleeding. Many and many a time I cried with the pain and the awful monotony of the job. But my mother's cheery, indomitable, uncomplaining nature was a great encouragement to us both and always, when the night's proportion was tackled—sometimes very late in the evening when the ropes and hawsers had been more difficult to tease than usual—we kissed each other and "cuddled up" out of sheer thankfulness.

It was while we were living in Arbroath that I started to sing. Like many more people in the world I have always been rather fond of hearing my own voice! Even as a very small boy I used to imitate my father when he hummed or sang some of the old Scottish lyrics. I cannot say that my father was a good vocalist because I don't remember. But he was aye croonin' awa' at some snatch of melody. One day he turned to my mother and said, "This wean's going to be a singer, Isa!" And he thereupon began to teach me the words and melody of "Draw the Sword, Scotland." I had as much idea of what drawing a sword for Scotland meant as of Greek Iambics—and if I was on the scaffold today I couldn't tell you what *these* are, but I saw the words in a book I happened to pick up yesterday! So I learned this song and one or two others, including a most melancholy ditty entitled, "I'm a Gentleman Still." The tune to which this song was set had an extremely sorrowful wail about it and it became a sort of obsession with me. It never left me for years. I would start singing or humming it at any time and in any circumstances. You know the sort of thing I mean—a tune takes hold of you to such an extent that you simply can't get it out of your head. You begin to hate the damnable iteration of its cadences. You try your best to forget it. But it is impossible. That's how it was with me so far as this song was concerned. And one night an event happened which was to focus this dreadful song even more firmly in my mind.

My mother had insisted on my joining the Band of Hope. Probably she had noted very early symptoms of depravity in me in the way of an affection for tobacco and thought that I would be safeguarded from other vices by "signing the pledge" and coming under the influence of the Blue Ribbon Army. In these days the Scottish teetotallers and the Band of Hope boys all wore a blue ribbon to demonstrate to the world their detestation of strong drink. If you

were an abstainer you were a member of the Blue Ribbon
Army, as it was then called.

The Band of Hope meetings I loved. They were bright
and colourful. The officials were good men and women, full
of high ideals. The singing at the meetings appealed to me
from the start. Moody and Sankey, the American evangel-
ists, had left a deeply religious effect all over Britain and
the hymns they sang at their revival meetings had taken a
powerful grip of the people of Scotland. Their melodies were
simple but swinging; they lent themselves admirably to com-
munity singing. I forget many of the hymns we sang at the
Band of Hope, but such favourites as "Shall We Gather At
the River?" "Throw Out the Life-Line," and similar haunting airs stand out in my memory. I loved every note of them
and yelled them out most lustily. The old Scottish psalm
tunes we occasionally sang at the Band of Hope, and also at
the Sunday School I attended, likewise made an extraordinary appeal to me. "All People That On Earth Do Dwell," to
the tune of the Old Hundred; "O, God of Bethel By Whose
Hand," to the tune of Martyrdom, and "Do Thou With
Hysop Sprinkle Me," to the tune of St. Kilda, were among
my favourites. The last mentioned melody is in a most unusual minor key. It was written by a young Scottish musician
named Bloomfield who died early in life and whose body, I
have often been told, is lying in an ancient cemetery in
Aberdeen.

Middle-aged and elderly Scots who may happen to be
reading my memoirs will remember this tune of St. Kilda
and how whole congregations used to sway from side to
side as they were singing its plaintive ear-haunting rhythms.
And they will remember the old Precentor with his pitch-
fork—before the "chists o' whistles" (the organs and har-
moniums) were introduced—searching for the key and then
leading off the psalmody for the assembled worshippers.
His was a job second only in importance to that of the

"meenister" himsel'! Other old hymns which I loved to hear
announced were "Art Thou Weary, Art Thou Languid," by
J. M. Neale, "O, Love That Wilt Not Let Me Go," by Dr.
Matheson, the blind preacher, and "Lord of All Being
Throned Afar"—that gorgeous bit of poetic imagery by
Oliver Wendell Holmes, who would, to my mind, have been
the greatest hymn-writer in the world had he only written
some more. Yes, all these psalms and hymns made on me a
profound impression, especially on the musical side. I feel
sure they implanted in me that passion for melody which has
been the supreme thing in my life.

But to return to the incident I mentioned. At the Band
of Hope meetings it was the practice of the superintendent
to ask any of the boys or girls to stand up and sing or recite
any little thing they knew. For many weeks I was too shy to
"take the floor," but one night a companion who had evidently heard me singing at the mill or in the school playground nudged me in the ribs, saying, "Go on, Harry,
staun' up and dae somethin'." So up I got from my seat,
walked to the little platform and modestly said that I was
willing to sing a song. I had fully intended to sing "Draw
the Sword, Scotland," or "Annie Laurie," or one of the
other songs I had learned since leaving Mŭsselburgh. But
could I remember, facing my first audience, that any other
song existed in the world with the exception of "I'm a
Gentleman Still"? No, my mind went blank of everything
but this awful song and this is what I suddenly found myself singing in a high treble voice:

> Though poverty daily looks in at my door
> Though I'm hungry and footsore and ill,
> Thank God I can look the whole world in the face
> And say, I'm a Gentleman Still!

Surely no more incongruous spectacle could be imagined
than the little bare-footed half-timer from Gordon's Flax
Mill standing there proclaiming, in song, that though poor

(God knows!) he was a gentleman still! But I got a great reception. The Band of Hope children applauded me to the echo. There has been no sweeter moment in my life than when I finished the song and made my way back to the "form" with the hand-clapping and the shouting of my comrades ringing in my ears. I wouldn't have changed places that night with Queen Victoria or the President of the United States!

A few weeks later a travelling concert-party gave a performance at the Oddfellows' Hall. A feature of the evening was a "grand amateur competition for ladies and gentlemen." Abyssinian gold (?) watches were offered as prizes. The town was plastered with placards announcing the concert and the contest. Two pals of mine in the mill, Bob Hannah and Johnnie Yeamans—I remember their names quite well because the three of us were nearly killed together in a boiler explosion at a local sawmill—urged me to enter for the "Solid Abyssinian gold hunter watch." We glued our eyes so persistently on the pictures of the watch shown in a corner of the playbills that the three of us could not sleep for thinking of it. Bob and Johnnie, who had heard my triumph at the Band of Hope, were certain I would win the watch. I was their hero.

But their interest in the contest was not wholly impersonal it appeared, for their idea—boldly and brazenly announced—was that if I won we would sell the watch and divide the money. This suggestion got me in a tender part at once! The idea of anybody making money off me, through me, or by my efforts was highly repugnant to me then. And, to tell the truth, I don't think my views on this point have suffered any violent alteration up to the present day!

The upshot of the scheme, however, was that I entered for the competition and duly won the watch from a "field" of some ten or a dozen competitors all of whom were many years older than the trembling little half-timer who put his

whole soul into the words and music of "I'm a Gentleman
Still." One of the audience was the manager of the mill I was
employed at and at the finish of the competition he sent
round a shilling for Wee Harry Lauder. Hannah and Yeamans were waiting for me outside. They gave me a boisterous welcome but before they could introduce the matter of
selling my prize I told them bluntly that I wouldn't sell the
watch for any money, but that they could have the shilling.
Bob and Johnnie examined the watch most carefully, and
then decided that they would take the money! The watch
went splendidly for a week. Then it stopped, never to go
again, as the old song says. But I still have it. I handled it
lovingly only a night or two ago.

In another similar competition a month or two afterwards I again won the first prize, a six-bladed knife. As I
already had a knife—one I had found in the Abbey Path
when delivering papers early on a Saturday morning—I sold
this knife to a man in the mills for elevenpence. We argued
about the price for three days; I wanted two shillings, the
purchaser offered fourpence. Ultimately, we compromised on
the price stated. Had I not been by this time a hardened
smoker I do not think I would have sold the prize so cheaply
but elevenpence represented the price of three or four ounces
of Bogey Roll, now the only tobacco with a sufficient kick
in it for my thirteen-year-old palate!

After we had lived in Arbroath for about two years a
brother of my mother's who had settled in the Black Country, as the coal-mining district of the west of Scotland is
termed, wrote urging that she and her family should mi-
grate to Hamilton. There would be more opportunities there,
he pointed out, for the boys and also for the girls when
they grew up a bit. With seven hungry young mouths to
feed and bodies to clothe the problem that faced my poor
mother at this period must have been dire indeed. I was still
the only breadwinner, apart from her own tireless efforts,

and my pay was only about three shillings a week. In order
to add to the family income I tried several times to get employment as a full-timer in the mills. By telling the different
managers I was over fourteen I got started more than once,
but I was always caught out by the factory inspector and
packed back to half-time. How I hated that interfering
official! More than once I hid myself among the bales of
flax when I knew he was in the building, but if I escaped
detection one day, discovery was certain sooner or later.
The inspector seemed to have a special "down" on me
because I once heard him asking if that damned young
singin' rascal Harry Lauder was workin' here?

So it came about that when I was asked my opinion as
to the suggested move to the west I was all for it. We were
sorry to leave "dear old St. Tammas," as the town of Arbroath is affectionately known to its natives throughout the
world, but needs must when the devil drives and the next
chapter in my life begins at Hamilton, some ten or twelve
miles from Glasgow. Hamilton is the centre of one of the
greatest coal areas in Britain. There are dozens and dozens
of pits within a mile or two of the town, or of the surrounding towns and villages such at Coatbridge, Airdrie, Cambuslang, Shotts, Larkhall, Bothwell, etc.

The Lauder family settled down in an exceedingly humble habitation in one of the poorer quarters of the town.
My Uncle Sandy was a "bottomer" in Eddlewood Colliery
and one of his mates agreed to give me a start as his "boy"
in one of the seams of this famous colliery. My wages were
to be ten shillings a week—to me an unheard-of sum and
almost too good to be true. As a matter of fact, it *was* too
good to be true, because my "gaffer" disappeared with all
the money at the end of the first week, and was never seen
in Hamilton again. That Saturday night I cried myself to
sleep. My first week's work in the damp, dark depths of the
mine had left me sore in every limb and muscle of my body.

And to be done out of my week's wages to which I had been looking forward with feverish eagerness was the last straw. My mother sat on the edge of my bed and cried with me! I was a broken-hearted laddie. But we got over this terrible disaster as we had surmounted many more serious.

I went back to the pit-head on the Monday morning to look for another job. The first man I met was Gibbie (Gilbert) Pitcairn, the general manager at Eddlewood. I told him of my experience with the fraudulent miner and he clapped me on the back, telling me to keep a stout heart and saying I would be a good collier yet. Under a rough exterior Gibbie was a splendid man; he stood four-square to the world and feared neither owner nor miner. He started me right away to help shift the wagons at the pit-head. Later in the day he was passing that way. He stood and watched me for a few minutes. I was evidently doing my work in a slip-shod or frightened manner. "Here, you," he cried in a voice like a fog-horn, "Come here!" I advanced in terror. Looking me up and down he asked, "Do ye ken a' that ye need, ma lad?" "No, sir," I replied. "The horns, by God!" he growled —and passed on. This indication that I was full brother to a goat left me in great tribulation, but I learned from one of the men that Gibbie's bark was far worse than his bite. In after years he was one of my greatest friends and admirers.

That week I earned nine shillings. I ran all the way home and proudly placed the money in my mother's lap. What a different Saturday night that was from the previous one! My mother and I counted the money over and over again. My brothers and sisters all had a look at it and said with bated breaths—"Harry's pey!" A shilling of the money went on 2d. Mince pies, a whole one each for the four oldest and a half each for the little ones! I was now the real head of the family, the principal breadwinner for the eight of us. My age at this time was thirteen and a half.

After a week or two at the pit-head Gibbie Pitcairn found

a job for me down below as a trapper. The trapper's duty is to open and shut the wooden trap-doors controlling the air supply to admit of the hutches passing out and in. It would take too long to describe just what these air-course "traps" stand for in the matter of safety and a proper current of air hundreds of fathoms below the surface of the soil. In any case the trapper is supposed never to leave his post of duty for a moment. Occasionally, however, I helped the pony drivers with their "tubs" over bad bits of road or round awkward bends and switches. You see I was anxious to be promoted pony-driver myself and I took every opportunity of becoming versed in their work and in the control of the brave and tremendously wise little horses who were doomed to spend their lives in the black deeps of a coal-mine.

I don't suppose I was any more humane in my instincts than the rest of the boys at Eddlewood but I well remember the first time I came to blows with a boy a few years older than myself. As he came through my "trap" with a load of well-filled hutches he jabbed his pony in the ribs with an iron rod he had picked up at the foot of the shaft. The little thing winced under the cruel blow. It was more than I could stand. "Hughie," I said, "if I see you do that again I'll punch you in the jaw! Hittin' a puir wee pownie that canna hit back!" The driver didn't wait for any more "sauce" from me but landed me one on the ear. Thereon I kicked him in the stomach. The next "rake o' hutches" came along before he was able to proceed. We were the best of friends afterwards. My pay as a trapper was fifteen shillings a week —half-a-crown a day.

After a year I got the chance of a job as driver in Cadzow Colliery. The wages were a pound a week. We still lived at Eddlewood Buildings in a wee house the rent of which was three shillings a week. I had the better part of a mile to walk to and from my new job, but as the wages were so much better I did not mind this in the slightest. Besides, I was delighted to be "among the horses." What wonderful little fellows they were! Strong, game, and brimful of intelligence, the pit ponies interested me every hour of the day and night. Alas, *they* have no day or night; all their work is done by "shifts." But they know Saturday night when it comes along as well as the men they work beside! They are quite frisky when they are taking the last "rake" of the week to the bottom of the shaft and I am sure they would kick up their heels then if there was only room for them to do so.

I had one splendid little pony at Cadzow. He was named "Captain." He and I got to be very thick. In fact, like me and the general in "She's My Daisy," I think he was the thickest of the two! Standing eleven hands high he was a picture of health and strength although he had been "doon the dook" for several years. He knew every word that was spoken to him. His face was more expressive than many a man's I have known. I loved "Wee Captain" with my whole heart. The tricks I taught him! And the others he had picked up before he and I foregathered! He could count the number of times we had been to "the face" for a load. By what process of reasoning, or instinct, he did so none of us had the slightest idea. But if I said to him late in the shift "how many loads, Captain?" he would paw on the ground with his right foot and the number was never wrong! He also knew to within a minute or two when "lowsin' time" was due; could you have got Captain to go back for another rake of hutches after hours?—no, sir, not unless you explained to him very thoroughly just why this extra trip was necessary!

I taught my four-footed pal to steal, too. The place where the drivers leave their coats and caps is called the cabin. Into this cabin I used to take Captain and give him little tit-bits out of my own jacket and bits of bread and cheese from the "pieces" of the men on duty in different parts of the mine. All the flasks containing tea or coffee were left on the cabin floor and Captain soon learned to pick out a nice full flask, put it between his fore-hoofs and pull the cork with his teeth. This accomplished it was an easy matter for him to raise the flask and have a "swig" of tea or coffee! There were occasional rows about the miners' flasks being tampered with, but I said nothing. Whenever "Wee Captain" was on a foraging expedition in the cabin, he kept his ears cocked. If any other footfall than my own sounded near at hand he was out of the door like a shot and back either to his stable or his "road."

Once this dear little chap saved my life. He and I were on our way to the coal face with a "rake" of empty hutches. We had to pass a "drift"—an old working that has fallen in and been cut through, leaving above a fearsome-looking vaulty space twenty or thirty or forty feet high. I always felt creepy when we came to this great, gloomy cavern, and I think Captain did the same. In any case we always rushed it. But there came a time when the pony stopped dead just in front of the drift. Without thinking what I was doing I urged him to get on with the job in hand. He still refused. I gave him a sharp cut with my little whip. Wincing, he looked round and stared me full in the face. "What's wrong, Captain?" I asked. Simultaneously with the question I heard the most terrifying sound that can assail the miner's ears—the creak and groan of the world above him before the earth and stone comes crashing down to fill the vacuum. Captain turned completely round in his tracks, pulling one of the hutches off the rails and sought the comparative safety of the tunnel we were just about to leave. I did the same. Next moment five hundred tons of material fell with a noise like thunder into the cavern in front of us. How near we both were to disaster may be judged by the fact that the hutch pulled round off the rails by the pony was afterwards found

to be filled with jagged stones and rock! Safe in the tunnel I
turned and hugged and kissed Captain again and again. His
sensitive ears had heard the warning before I did. He knew
what to do—and in doing it he saved both our lives. Years
afterwards I would have given my right hand to have been
able to buy Captain and present him with his freedom in
God's sunlight. But he died in the pit, as he had lived in it.
Brave heart! I have forgotten many men and I'll forget
many more. I shall never forget "Wee Captain!"

CHAPTER FOUR

IN THE COAL-PITS

As TIME went on I tackled all sorts of jobs in the pit. You may be sure that if there was an extra shilling or two to be picked up anywhere, and at any work, hard or easy, I was well after the money! For months I acted as a water-drawer in the well-known Allenton Colliery. Some pits are wet and some dry. Allenton was a very wet pit in my time and the water was so bad in the lower workings that "drawers" were employed at night to remove it. This was done by baling the water into wagons; the ponies pulled these to the "top of the rise" where the plugs below the wagons were released. This water was afterwards pumped out by the great pumps at the pit bottom. Night after night I was the only boy on duty at Allenton. Forty or fifty tons of water had to be removed each night so there was no time to "dawdle"; it was hard graft for ten hours with only a brief "piece-time" interval. And wasn't it drear and lonely! I had to sing to keep my spirits up. I even made friends with the pit-rats—great, grim, phosphorous-eyed creatures that gathered round you as you ate your piece and fought each other like miniature lions for the crusts.

One night I came across a thousand of these monstrous rats moving from one part of the colliery to another. I got it into my head that they had made up their minds to make a massed attack on me. Horror took possession of me and I ran shrieking to the place half a mile away where the only other living soul in the pit was working. This was Jamie McCulloch, the roadman. Jamie quietly stilled my fears by assuring me that the "rodents" were harmless, that they

55

liked the companionship of man and that they never had been known to attack anybody in the mines.

"Come on, Harry," he finished up, "let's hae a sing-sang thegither. That'll keep us cheery!" And there, each seated on the ground or on a lump of coal, we sang whatever songs we knew. Jamie was a student of poetry and could quote long "screeds" of Burns, Walter Scott, Hogg, the Ettrick shepherd, and Tannahill, the weaver poet of Paisley. I learned to like these poets too, and not long afterwards I was delighted to get a loan of several of Jamie's books the contents of which I eagerly devoured.

To Jamie, and another extraordinary character whom I first met in the pits, Rab MacBeth, I think I owe my determination to keep up my singing. At least, both men encouraged me to sing to them and their evident enjoyment of it pleased me more than I can tell. Rab MacBeth was really a worthy—one of the most amusing and original fellows in Lanarkshire and he had the reputation of being just about the best all-round miner in the shire. Big and brawny, with a voice like a bull and a laugh like a peal of deep-toned bells, he added a most quaint touch of humour to his other faculties. He was one of my first "gaffers." While he hewed the coal I drew it back from the "face" and filled it into the empty hutches. We were working, I remember, in a very wet place and while Rab was comparatively dry, digging as he was on a sort of ledge above me, I was "plowtering" about all day up to my thighs in water. I must have complained about the discomfort and misery of it all—I forget how it came to arise—but Rab stopped his hewing, looked down at me and yelled out in his great booming voice, "Well, sing, ye wee devil! Singin' and whisky's the best things to mix wi' watter."

Rab MacBeth's father before him had been a character in Hamilton. The story is told about the old man having wandered into the local "geggie" (any portable theatre thrown up on a waste piece of ground) when the play "Macbeth" was being produced. He had the idea that some of his own family were being portrayed in the play. For a long time he sat and watched the action without ever saying a word. Then when Macduff killed Macbeth, old Rab rose in his seat, pointed a scornful finger at the dead Macbeth lying on the stage and cried out "What a lot o' dam' nonsense! You're no a real Macbeth or you wouldna' let a —— man like that (pointing in turn to Macduff) kill you! Besides, yer accent's a wrang—I don't believe yer a Macbeth at a'." With that he stalked out of the theatre in high dudgeon.

His son was also a great admirer of the drama; at least he was very fond of going to see all the travelling companies that came round Hamilton way. He was also a singer of sorts and had there been prizes for the biggest voices, Rab, Junior, would have scooped the pool. Once he went down to the Broomilaw at Glasgow to see his brother "Wull" away to Australia. From the quay-side he kept on shouting good-byes in such an ear-splitting voice that the other spectators had to put their hands up to protect their aural organs from destruction. As the steamer moved away from the pier Rab's stentorious shoutings to his relative became louder and louder. "Good-bye, Wull, mind, an' write! DINNA FORGET TO WRITE, WULL! *IF YE DINNA WRITE, WULL, I'LL NEVER SPEAK TO YE AGAIN!*" And so on, every command to write getting louder and louder as the ship edged further and further down the Clyde. At last a man standing near turned to Rab and said, "There'll be nae need for Wull to write; just roar a bit louder, ye ——, and he'll hear you in Australia!"

Two or three years after I had been his boy at the coal-face, Rab met me in the street one day and told me that he was giving a grand competition concert in one of the local halls and that if I would enter for the "comics" he would see

that I won the first prize. By this time I had achieved a
certain measure of fame in Hamilton and vicinity as a
comedian and Rab's confident prediction that I would win
the first prize encouraged me to put in my name for the
contest. When the night came along the hall was packed.
I heard afterwards that there was fifteen pounds "in the
house" and that Rab had himself sold most of the tickets
beforehand. He himself had entered for one of his own
prizes in the "bass or baritone" section. In addition he
acted as master of the ceremonies.

The first singer he announced was a tenor who started
to sing, in a key an octave too high for him, an operatic
solo entitled "When Other Lips." He had not completed
the first line of the song when his voice cracked and there
was such a torrent of jeers and sneers that the poor devil
was glad to rush off the stage. After a girl had struggled
through a sentimental song another male vocalist took her
place almost before the few half-hearted cheers for the previous competitor had died away. This fellow was a baritone and his song began with the assertion that he was a
soldier and a man. As he was a weedy individual in a
solemn black suit with a sixpenny tie attached by a hook
to his collar-stud and was wearing steel-framed spectacles,
the audience simply refused to accept his statement.

He, too, got no further than the opening bars of his song
and was glad to beat a speedy retreat to the safety of the
anteroom. By this time the audience was in high fettle.
They settled down to a regular feast of bear-baiting. But
the effect upon the waiting competitors was calamitous.
They all had the wind up. Rab, as boss of the concert,
ordered another man to "go on and paralyse 'em." He
refused—being already half-paralysed himself—and ran out
of the hall.

The same thing happened with the next competitor. In
his extremity Rab asked me to take the platform, and,

shaking in every limb, I did so. The most I can say is that I got through my song, a burlesque ditty about a man who had bought a grand new coat for ninepence, without anything being thrown at me and that I was glad to get away from the footlights minus personal injury.

By this time there were only about five contestants left in the wings. All the others had packed up and slunk away. So Rab decided to go on himself and sing a song. He was even less successful than the opening "artistes" for whenever he showed face he was received with a chorus of moans, groans, and rude noises. But Rab was brave. He stood his ground. Three times he tried to start his vocal performance; each time he had to stop. My own "turn" over I stood in the wings convulsed with merriment as I watched Rab getting angrier and angrier. He began to harangue the audience and so powerful was his voice that its tones rang out above and beyond the combined din of the now thoroughly delighted audience. At first he accused some of the "auld toon" men of causing the disturbance, then he went on to state that the people in front were missing some of the finest talent ever assembled in Hamilton—a statement which was received with screams of derision!—and finally, losing his rag completely, he extended his fingers to his nose and challenged any three men in the audience to come up on the platform and fight him! As a matter of fact, one or two groups of miners showed rather a willingness to accept his invitation when the lights in the hall suddenly went out. The concert terminated in chaos and some free fights. Not until several weeks afterwards did I hear that Rab himself had given secret orders to the hallkeeper to turn out the lights soon after he went on the platform. The wily rascal had seen how the wind was blowing and thought this was the best end to a venture which had earned him a nice bit of "ready" but which was a dire failure as a singing competition!

Many, many years later I was performing at the Odean Theatre, St. Louis, and immediately I danced on to the platform to sing "Tobermory," a terrific voice cried out, "Come on, Harry, let them see what the wee collier laddie frae Hamilton can dae! Harry, ma cock—up an' at them!"

I couldn't see the speaker. But I could never mistake the voice.

"A' richt, Rab," I shouted up to the gallery, "I'll dae ma best. See you round in the dressing-room after the show!"

Of course it proved to be my old gaffer Rab, settled down and doin' well, like so many of his compatriots, in a great American city. Whenever he entered my room, he rushed at me, lifted me as if I had been a baby and shed tears of delight over our romantic meeting after twenty years! On recovering his composure he solemnly presented me with a pair of "galloses"—braces! Poor Rab! He died some years ago.

The mining industry in Lanarkshire has been almost completely transformed since I worked in the pits there. Coal-cutting machinery has done away with what might be called the individual touch in the industry. It is quite true that we had Unions in the early days. I was a member of the Lanarkshire Union of Miners, a strong supporter of men like Bob Smillie and Kier Hardie. But politics were not mixed up in industrial affairs as they are today. Besides, there seemed to be a far greater measure of freedom for a man to work as hard as he liked and as long as he liked for the benefit of his own pay-roll and the increased comfort of himself and his family which the fat pay-roll represented. With few exceptions every man in the pit in these days was a hard, conscientious worker. He worked hard and he played hard. I would not go the length of saying that we were all contented with our lowly lot, but we seemed to believe in the old Scriptural injunction that only by the sweat of our brows could we eat bread. And, by God, we sweated right enough.

As each of my brothers reached twelve years of age they left the school and went down below. Matt was the first for whom I found a job, and then Jock, Alec, and George followed in due time. Matt was a chap like myself, as strong as a lion and a keen willing worker. He and I teamed up together by and by. And didn't we make the coal fly from the seam when we specially wanted to have a good week's pay. As I have said, those were the days—believe me, the happy days—when a miner was only proud of getting what he had worked for. Take all you can get and give as little as you feel inclined seems to be the motto of too many people all over the world today.

It's wrong! It's all wrong! It is demoralizing in every direction. It is unjust to the good, honest workman; it has a softening, deadening influence on the boy or man whose heart is the slightest bit out of its natural position. Recently, both in Britain and America, I have been preaching the gospel of "free trade" in brawn and brains, the creed of letting a man earn as much as he wants to within reasonable limitations. In America the system has been adopted very widely. But in this country trade and industry are being hampered, and initiative and ambition stifled by "ca' canny, take everything and give as little as possible!"

Matt and I worked so hard that we came to be known as the "Coal Mawks"—the coal worms that bored away and bored away, ceaselessly and persistently. If there was a difficult or dangerous job we were "on it like a cock at a gooseberry"—always granted that the money was all right, mind you! The two brothers put up some amazing records in coal-getting. I have myself cut from five to six tons of coal in a shift. That was at the soft coal, while at the poyt-shaw coal, twenty-nine or thirty inches in thickness, and

with little room to swing your pick, I have reckoned a ton
and a half an excellent day's work.

While still in my teens I became a contractor. You have
to be a responsible and experienced miner before you are
allowed to take on a job by contract. It was at Barncleuth
and Silverton Collieries that I got my first contract to drive
a level from Will Frew, the underground manager. The
system adopted in fixing a contract is simplicity itself. The
manager takes you along to a certain working in the mine
and says, "Gie me an offer?" You examine the coal-face,
the quality of the coal, the depth of the seam, the arrangements for haulage and wooding, etc., and on these facts
you make a quick mental calculation. On this occasion I
offered Frew to take on the job at six-and-sixpence a fathom.
"Done!" said he, and we shook hands—as binding an agreement as if the deed had been drawn up by a dozen lawyers
and witnessed before the Court of Session. "A spittle in
the loof an' a shak' o' the hand," as the old Scottish phrase
has it, has sealed more honourably kept bargains in Scotland
than were ever attested on parchment in any other country
in the world.

In my day a miner's word was his bond. It may still be.
I hope so, anyhow. I suppose there are still "contractors" in
the Scottish mines, but, as I have said, the machines have
altered everything and coal-cutting is not now the real man's
work that it used to be. Incidentally, I learned long after
leaving the pits for the stage that in several of the Lanarkshire collieries there were "still places" below known as
"Lauder headings" and "Lauder levels," a tribute to my reputation and industry as a miner which I value very much
indeed.

CHAPTER FIVE

I LOVE A LASSIE

I WOULD be about eighteen when I started to "love a lassie"! The tender passion comes early to the boys and girls in the Black Country. At least it did so in my time. We were men and women at sixteen and seventeen. School days were left far behind. We were battling for bread at an age which today would be looked upon as childhood. I was "boss o' the hoose" when I was thirteen; a year or two later I was a man earning a man's pay and with a man's outlook on life. Was it to be wondered at, therefore, that I early fell under the spell of two bonnie blue eyes and a mass of dark curls when the former flashed a look at me from a Salvation Army "ring" in the Black's Well one Sunday afternoon? I was smitten on the spot. I was captured and enraptured. It was love at first sight—first, last, and only. Annie Vallance—Nance! It's just on forty years ago, but I can scarcely write the dear name for the feelings that memory causes to surge within me. If ever a bonnie lassie knocked a young fellow "tapsalteerie" (literally, dizzy) fourteen-year-old Annie Vallance did me! I couldn't eat the first night I saw her, I couldn't sleep, and the next day I couldn't work! I had got it bad. Oh, dear me! I thought I was going to die. But there's aye a Providence in these things. I managed to get an introduction through one of her young brothers. For Tom Vallance I have had a very soft side from that day to this. I taught him his job as a miner and he is now, as he has been for thirty years, my faithful friend and manager. Where I go Tom goes. I do nothing without consulting him. He is almost as well known all over the world as I am!

Did the course of true love run smooth in our case? I don't know that it did. There were lots of chaps after Nance, but I told her plump and plain that I would fight anybody who tried to take her from me. Yes, I would kill any three men in Hamilton who dared to look at her! As for Nance herself—if ever I saw her turn a "keek" in any other direction—well it would be the worse for her. This sheikh stuff did not go down well with the young lady, but that it had some slight effect I still flatter myself to this day. But sweethearts we soon became. Sweethearts we remain.* Once I was interviewed by a prominent American journalist who said he wanted to get my views on divorce problems. What I told him was this, "I don't know anything at all about divorce problems. I've been coming to the States for twenty years and I always bring the same wife with me!"

To consolidate my position, so to speak, I got a job at Number 7 Pit in the Quarter, a village close to Hamilton. The underground manager was Nance's father, Jamie Vallance. At first he did not know anything about me or that I was courting his daughter. He was a stern, dignified but straightforward man. No liberties were tolerated by "Jammuck"—in these days he was as good with his "jukes" as any prizefighter and any of the "younkers" who thought they had an easy mark to deal with in him speedily learned their mistake. Every man at the Quarter held the underground manager in a mixture of fear and wholesome respect and esteem. I know I did.

For months I did everything I could to earn Jamie's good opinion. I worked very hard and had always a cheery time-a-day for the boss when he came along the workings or I met him above ground. Nance would now

---

* Since writing the earlier part of these memoirs my darling wife has been taken from me. She died suddenly in Glasgow in August 1927. I cannot bring myself to alter in any shape or fashion the many tender references to her throughout these pages.　　　　　　H. L.

M. Pearlmann & Co., Glasgow
SIR HARRY AT NINETEEN

SIR HARRY AND LADY LAUDER TWENTY-FIVE YEARS AGO

be about seventeen and I about twenty. My brothers and sisters were all working. Plenty of money was going into our house. There was no more call for me to hand over all my pay to my mother. I determined to get married. Nance was quite willing, but in her case she realized a difficulty. She was the eldest girl in the family, her own mother's mainstay and there was a troop of younger brothers and sisters to be cared for and "raised." Neither of us knew just how the "auld folks"—not yet forty themselves, by the way—would take the proposition; we were nervous of broaching it.

But one Saturday night I happened to meet the manager down-town. He was in a genial mood. We stood and "clavered" for a while and then I invited Mr. Vallance to have a refreshment in the bar of the Royal Hotel. He indicated his willingness to partake of my hospitality, but I could see from the look he gave me that he was wondering whether I had started to drink beer at my comparatively early age. However, when I ordered a lemonade for myself and a "wee hauf" for him, he thawed considerably.

"Now or never!" said I to myself, and there and then I told him, nervously but without any waste of words, that I was in love with his daughter, Nance, and wanted to marry her right away. Jamie eyed me up and down without saying a word. He took a deep breath or two. I looked anxiously towards the door suddenly remembering all the stories I had heard about his quick temper. Should I run for it while the going was good? Then he turned to the bar attendant and slowly ordered "the same again." I was saved—for the time being.

After drinking his "nip," the manager put his hand on my shoulder and said, "Harry, ma lad, ye've put a sair problem to me this nicht! Answer me a'e question—do ye love her?" With tears in my eyes I replied that I loved her with a' ma heart and that I would try my best to mak' her happy.

"Swear it, Harry!" said he.

"I swear it, Jamie!" I answered, and lifted my right hand.

We were silent for a moment or two. Then the manager turned to me again and said, "Harry, if there's love in the camp atween you and oor Nance, tak' her an' joy be wi' ye! But," he added quickly, "ye'll hae to ask her mither first!"

I couldn't get out of the hotel quick enough; Nance was waiting for me round the corner. We were both overjoyed at the result of the interview with her father. There would be no trouble with the mother, Nance assured me, for that good lady, with the intuition of every true mother, knew all about our little romance. Do you mind, Nance, that we stayed out till nearly eleven that night? That we strolled up and down the Lanark Road about nineteen times not knowing what we were doing or saying, or where we were going? How I told you I was determined to be a great man one day and make you a lady, with silk gowns to wear, a carriage-and-pair to ride in, and a big house to live in with double doors and hot water laid on? Do you mind how you laughed and said I was daft, but that I was your own Harry Lauder and that nothing else mattered? You will remember all that perhaps, but neither you nor I can remember how often we kissed each other, how often we looked in each other's eyes, how often we sighed and cuddled up closer and closer!

"Aw, cut out this sob stuff, Harry!" I can hear some of you chaps saying as you read my last page or two. But I can't. It's in my bones. I know I'm a sentimental old duffer now. I've been sentimental all my life—Nance made me so in the first instance, and she still keeps me full of sentiment today.

Long courtships are not encouraged in the mining dis-

tricts of Scotland and when Nance and I had been "walkin'
out" for a few months we decided to get married as soon
as we could find a house. Fortunately we met with no difficulty in this direction. The colliery proprietors I was working for at the time had a house vacant in the Weaver's Land,
a colony of miners' residences owned and controlled by
them. The rent was three and sixpence a week, which sum
was kept off the weekly pay envelope. As I was working on
"contract" and earning about three pounds a week the rent
could not be considered excessive. Moreover, I had always
been of a saving disposition, especially since falling in love,
and had over twenty pounds in the bank, a sum more than
ample to set us on our feet as a young married couple. The
vacant but-and-ben having been repainted and papered, we
started to furnish the humble nest right away.

The main article of furniture which engrossed our most
earnest attention was the kitchen dresser. No working man's
house in Scotland in those days was complete without a
dresser. This is a highly polished wooden contraption with
two swinging doors in front and a "back" rising above the
level of the top boarding. Her dresser was—and still is so
far as I know—the special joy and pride of the Scottish
housewife. In its shelves below, and outside on top, she
displays her crockery and ornaments and table equipment
to the best advantage. As often as not a doyley is spread
outside and on this ornamentation the clock, or a pair of
vases, or a couple of toddy bowls are placed with an eye
to effect. The whole thing is kept as shiny and spotless
as possible. The first thing the visitor to the miner's home
does is to examine the dresser with a most critical eye; it
is the keynote to the taste, the cleanliness and the general
housewifely qualities of the lady in command.

As I have said, Nance and I spent a lot of time and
thought over the purchase of our dresser. But at last the
die was cast—we selected one which cost us three pounds ten

shillings. It was a beauty. Dark-stained and so perfectly polished that we could see our faces in the wood. We were so enamoured of this marvellous piece of furniture that we went back to the cabinetmaker's shop again and again just to make sure that he hadn't sold it. And immediately the house was ready for us the dresser was installed with much formality and care. A bed, bedclothes, a table and some chairs, together with a paraffin lamp and a strip of carpet to go in front of the fireplace practically completed our purchases for the house; the little extras such as a clock, ornaments, knives and forks and spoons we knew we would get as wedding presents!

If I remember rightly I spent less than fifteen pounds on furnishing our first house, which meant that I was left with the handsome margin of about five pounds for eventualities. I was so anxious to complete the home that I carried practically all the "plenishings" from the shops to the Weaver's Land. Even the kitchen table was transported on my head, its legs sticking up in the air, and I laugh now as I recollect the amount of banter I had to submit to from friends and acquaintances as I trudged down the main street.

A couple of weeks before the marriage our wee house was "as neat as ninepence." You could have taken your breakfast off the floor, as we say in Scotland. Nance's mother was the guiding spirit in getting the habitation ship-shape. Night after night she and I went along and we scrubbed and polished, polished and scrubbed until every mortal thing in the place shone like a mirror. I was so happy that I danced and sang as we worked. And wasn't I the proud young fellow when I took my young wife home to her "ain hoose" for the first time!

After being "cried" in the Parish Church for three weeks and having the banns posted at the Registrar's window for a like period (we went down town every night and stood reading this solemn document until we knew every word of it by heart) we were married in the Vallance home in The Bent, Hamilton, on the eighteenth day of June, 1890. Nance looked a picture in a new white dress I had given her as my marriage gift. She also wore a wee poke bonnet with red ribbons tied beneath her chin. My! but she was bonnie. I don't know how I looked, but I know that I had on my Sunday suit with a stiff white shirt—the first I ever possessed—a standing-up peaked collar and a very loud tie with green spots on a yellow background. On my feet was a pair of gutta percha shoes, half leather and half canvas. The whole outfit, barring the suit, which I had had for some months, cost me less than ten shillings at Harry Wilson's, the local outfitter.

Doubtless I was in the height of fashion for a miner's wedding at that time, but my own opinion is that a minister of today would refuse to marry a man accoutred as I was at the "altar"—my father-in-law's plush-covered parlour table! When the time came for me to produce the ring I was so excited and nervous that I could not get it out of my waistcoat pocket for quite a long time. Ultimately I unearthed it from among a mixture of odds and ends such as a knife, a plug of tobacco, a broken pipe and a piece of string! The incident, accompanied as it was by the tittering of my brothers and sisters, almost brought me to a state of collapse. Long years afterwards I made good use of it as a bit of stage-play in my song "Roamin' in the Gloamin'."

After the ceremony was all over we adjourned to the Lesser Victoria Hall where the marriage "spree" took place. Our marriage was what is known in Scotland as a "pay-waddin' "—all the outside guests paid for their tickets. Most marriages in the Black Country forty years ago were conducted on these highly sensible lines. Men with marriageable daughters had no money wherewith to give fancy wedding parties. If you wanted to attend a friend's marriage you cheerfully "paid your whack." In our case, the price was

fixed at eight-and-six-pence the double ticket. The two
families drew up lists of probable well-wishers and issued
invitations to them, marking the financial obligation very
clearly on the "invite." My brother, Matt, who was my
best man, and Nance's sister, Kate, who acted as best
maid, sold thirty double tickets and they joyfully reported
to me that they could have sold as many more had the
hall been big enough to accommodate the extra number.

Like the wedding of Sandy MacNab, our "do" was a
swell affair! There were lashings of steak pie, chappit
tatties, rice pudding, tea and pastries. There was beer
in abundance for all who wished it. And there were bottles
of Scotch for the "heid yins" at the top table. "Jamie"
presided over the function. He said a brief grace and
ordered the assembled company to "fa' tae!" (English—get
busy on the grub!) They required no second bidding. Some
of the young miners had refrained from eating any food for
a day or two so that they could do full justice to the steam-
ing pies, the endless plates of potatoes and cabbage and car-
rots and the enormous helpings of rice and raisin pudding.
The fun and clatter became fast and furious; the din was
deafening.

Nance and I sat together at the foot of the main table.
We were very much in love, but we had both hearty appe-
tites, and we tucked in with the best and bravest of them—
at least, I did. After the tables were cleared there were
speeches and toasts. My health and the health of the bride
were duly toasted. Then the chairman sang a song, "Norah,
the Pride of Kildare," only stopping twice or three times
in the middle of it to implore silence from some of the more
obstreperous spirits who had started arguments about how
much coal they could cut if the "face" was workable at all!

In any social gathering of miners the conversation generally gets down to coal-cutting! Millions of mythical tons
must have been "cut" on the night I was married! Then

old Sandy Lennox was called upon for a song. Sandy had an extraordinary big nose which always seemed to be insecurely attached to his "dial" and when he sang he had a habit of shaking his head. This made his nose wobble in the most comical fashion. He had not sung more than half a dozen words when all the company were convulsed by the antics of his nose so he sat down in high dudgeon, which was only mollified by a good stiff "nip" passed along to him from a crony at the top table. I sang "Annie Laurie" and "Scotland Yet" and everybody who could sing or recite, or do anything at all was called upon in due course. By eleven o'clock the "conversations" was declared at an end. Then the dancing was started and was kept up, with constant hoochs and skirls and screeches until four or five in the morning.

I would not take the responsibility of asserting that all the wedding party were strictly sober when the early hours arrived, but I can truthfully say that everybody enjoyed themselves to the full. So much so, that when Nance and I quietly "jookit awa'" from the hall about three o'clock in the morning, we were never missed! And that is a fairly accurate description of a "pay-waddin'" in Scotland forty years ago.

Next morning, a Saturday, Nance and I were up early and off to Glasgow for our honeymoon—of one day's duration! We spent most of the time in McLeod's Wax Works in the Trongate, standing spell-bound before the effigies of Charlie Peace, Burke and Hare, and other notorious robbers and scoundrels and murderers! What a honeymoon! But in those days a visit to the Wax Works was considered one of the greatest treats to which a man could entertain his wife or his sweetheart. Later we went for a run on the top of a tram-car to the gates of Barlinnie Prison after which we wandered down to the Broomilaw, had a sniff of the Clyde, and this finished the day for us in more ways than one!

Tired, but completely happy and contented, we got back to Hamilton and "oor ain fireside!" We were "kirkit" the next day and on the Monday morning I was up at five o'clock and off to drive another yard or two of the Lauder Level in Allenton Colliery.

CHAPTER SIX

FIVE SHILLINGS TO A POUND

ALTHOUGH I was a very enthusiastic lover and spent several evenings every week with my bonnie wee Nance I did not neglect my singing. As a matter of fact I was always in great demand for local concerts all round the district. Generally there was a prize to compete for. It seems strange to think that this form of entertainment was once so popular in the towns and villages of Scotland. Nowadays it is as dead as the dodo—whatever that may mean.

But in my time as a boy and young miner in the West of Scotland these singing competitions were all the rage. Remember that this was long before the days of cinemas in little mining towns and villages. An occasional concert in the local hall, or drama in the "geggie" (provided by touring companies) was all the entertainment the people had to keep them from absolute boredom. Even the cheap-jacks that toured the industrial centres and sold their wares by public auction in the squares and at the street corners carried their own singers with them as a special attraction. Generally the vocalist was a low comedian. Whenever trade was dull the auctioneer stepped down from his "rostrum" and announced that his place would now be taken by "the famous London comedian So-and-So who would entertain the public free of all cost whatever!" Of course the people came trooping up to take advantage of this generous invitation.

One of the first comedians I heard perform from a travelling cheap-jack's van was a little man calling himself "Wee Harris." He was certainly very small and very comical in his costume and antics. He had a Glasgow accent that could have been cut with a knife. His songs did not err on the

73

side of delicacy, to say the least of it. His great "hit" was
a ditty about the indigestion troubles of the Duke of Argyll
and this song never failed to send the audience into fits of
hysterical laughter.

The public taste in those days was not nearly so refined
as it is now; I have seen the local policemen roar with merriment at Wee Harris's suggestive asides and jests. Today
they would probably "take action" in safeguard of public
morals and good taste. But Wee Harris was a sure draw
at all times and when he had collected a crowd and put them
all into good humour the auctioneer would again take up
his position and do a roaring trade. Singing contests were
frequently arranged by these gentry; the usual thing was to
stage a "grand open-air, free-entry contest to finish up a
very pleasant and successful week with our old friends in
Hamilton." The prizes to be won were shown on the stall
for several days beforehand.

I can remember with what admiration and envy I regarded a "magnificent solid-silver butter-cooler" which was
to be the premier award in the comic section of an amateur
contest arranged by a London auctioneer who had visited this
district for many years. I made up my mind to win this
gorgeous prize. Win it I did, and my mother was so delighted when I took it home that she started to polish it right
away. In a few minutes she had polished all the silver off it!
But she kept it in the house for years. I entered for many
of these al fresco contests on the public streets of the town
and won dozens of medals and cheap prizes, mostly household
ornaments such as vases, clocks, time-pieces, moustache-
cups—cups with a ridge inside the rim for preventing the
whiskers getting into the tea or coffee—fenders, fire-irons
and the like. Indeed at one time my mother's kitchen presented the appearance of a cheap-jack's store. She would
never throw out anything that "oor Harry" had won, but
when I was married I relieved her of some of the impedi-

menta and thus gave her room to walk freely about her
kitchen! The medals I wore on my watch-chain, much to
my own satisfaction and the unbounded admiration of my
brothers, sisters, and pals!

My reputation as a comedian had gradually spread. Invitations came rolling in for me to sing at all sorts of functions, soirees, football festivals, Saturday evening concerts,
church bazaars. I accepted them all. I was well rewarded
by the applause of my hearers, and if I got my train fare
paid when I visited outside towns and villages I was delighted. The first fee I ever received in my life was at
Larkhall. This was the modest sum of five shillings. But
had it been five pounds I couldn't have been a prouder man.
It was the first real step on the ladder of fame! I was
now something better than an amateur; people were ready
and willing to pay me for my talent! The thought intoxi-
cated me. If the hard-headed folks of Larkhall were prepared to pay, other concert promoters must do the same!
They did. Gradually I cut off all the gratuitous engagements. To every correspondent who wrote me asking for
my services I replied that I was not now accepting offers
without payment of a fee of five shillings, or ten shillings
or a pound as the case might be. To my immense delight
this did not stop them and engagements started to come in
with regularity which delighted me beyond measure.

The songs I had been singing up to this time were mostly
ballads, burlesques, and character stuff that had been sung
by other singers. I had also bought one or two choruses
and single verses from Glasgow song-writers. These did
not please me in their original shape and I altered and
twisted and re-wrote them until they made fairly presentable
numbers, full of grotesque comedy with patter and trimmings
to correspond.

Very early I began to appreciate the value of good
make-up. I took tremendous pains over every costume I

appeared in. The use of grease-paint and pencil and stick I studied as a student studies his books. For hours on end I practised the art of make-up in my mother's parlour and afterwards in my own house when I was married. I have spent an hour and a half making up for one character song before a concert. All my life I have gone on the principle that if a thing is worth doing it is worth doing as well as you know how to. If I saw a weird pair of trousers in a pawnbroker's window, or an old Paisley shawl, or a funny pair of elastic-sided boots, I saved up till I was able to buy the article I wanted. Often I would go into the shop and arrange with the proprietor to hold something over for me against the time I could pay for it.

One of the most important engagements that came my way as a boy of eighteen or nineteen was to sing at a concert in Edinburgh. This show was run by a well-known local comedian, Mr. R. C. McGill, who had evidently heard about my successes in Hamilton and district. He offered me a pound and my train fare—would I care to accept this fee? Would I accept it? I was at the station an hour before the train left for fear I would miss it! All the way through to Edinburgh I was rehearsing my songs, my patter, my facial expressions, trying my voice. As luck would have it I made a big hit that night with the Edinburgh folks. I sang three songs. They were "The Soor Dook Swimming Club," a nonsensical ditty about people bathing in buttermilk, "The Bleacher Lassies' Ball," a fantastic love song extolling the beauties of a girl who worked in a flax bleacher's field and was "so light and airt that she was just like a canary," and "Which of the Two is the Oldest—The Father or the Wean?" a lugubrious song describing the sorrows of a hen-pecked man left in charge of a precocious child. I could not repeat the words of these songs if you paid me to do it; they have gone, fortunately, completely from my memory.

But I know they made the people laugh uproariously and that was all I cared about.

After my "turn" was finished several of the local lyric-writers came round to see me, including Tom Glen, a Leith man who supplied many of the Scottish comedians, amateur and professional, with songs and patter. He and I became very friendly. He said my act was splendid, but my material weak—would I let him supply me with some ideas? "You've got what so few of them have, Harry," he said to me, "and that's personality. You made *me* laugh, and I haven't laughed at a Scotch comic for ten years! And I have got some notions you can set the heather on fire with!" This was all good hearing to me. Tom Glen was well known as an idea merchant and song writer and to have merited his unstinted praise was a feather in my cap. To cut a long story short, Tom supplied me with the ground-work of many songs thereafter. I bought from him to begin with, a quaint broken-down dude song called "Tooraladdie," which I sang all over the west of Scotland with unvarying success. I forget how the verses went, but the chorus was as follows:

> Twig Auld Tooraladdie,
> Don't he look immense?
> His watch and chain are no his ain,
> His claes (suit) cost eighteenpence.
> Wi' cuffs an' collar shabby,
> O' mashers he's the daddy
> Hats off! Stand aside
> An' let past Tooraladdie.

Awful rubbish, eh? I quite agree. But the verses were really funny and my make-up was enough to draw a smile from a Free Church elder. I set the song to an easy, jingling melody. It caught the public fancy and was hummed and sung by everybody. Another song I got from Glen—for a fee of five shillings, the same price as the first one—was entitled "Wha Died an' Left You the Coat?" This was also a grotesque song about a man whose uncle had died and left him a fortune—25s.—and an old coat, green with age and patched all over. Round about this time I started to write songs for myself, frequently taking an idea, for which I paid a few shillings, and twisting it round into a completely new song. This was what happened in the case of a song entitled "Mary Couldna' Dance The Polka," a female character study into which I introduced some droll dancing, and which always sent the lady members of my audience into fits of merriment.

But in my heart of hearts I was never satisfied with these early songs of mine. They were crude. I knew it. I made up my mind to produce better stuff. I realized that merely to redden one's nose, put on a ridiculous dress and cavort round the stage would never get me anywhere out of the rut of the five or ten shilling-a-night entertainer at purely local functions. And already I was having dreams of wider fields. I felt that if I could get together a repertoire of really good songs I might yet have a chance of making a successful attack upon the stage proper. An opportunity to this end was to present itself sooner than I had imagined or hoped for.

After doing a "turn" at a Saturday evening concert in Motherwell one of the artistes on the bill with me urged that I should send in my name as a competitor for a forthcoming "Great Comic Singing Contest" under the auspices of the Glasgow Harmonic Society. This was an organization of temperance people who ran Saturday evening "soirees," or tea-fights, as they were called, in three of the large public halls in different parts of the city. The main object of the promoters was to keep the working people off the street and out of the public-houses.

These entertainments had an amazingly successful vogue for many years. After the "tea and cookies" had been consumed a long and varied concert programme was put on. Frequently a vaudeville "star" of the first magnitude would be engaged from one or other of the local music-halls or brought up specially from London. On these nights the demand for tickets was tremendous. Another highly popular attraction was when an amateur competition was announced.

It was in connection with one of these contests that I made my first public appearance in Glasgow. I won the second prize, but, far more to the point, my success secured for me a series of engagements for other Harmonic concerts. The fee was one pound, and for this you had to sing at all three halls, free transport being provided by the organization. The audiences at these "Glesca Bursts"—thus the entertainments were vulgarly designated on account of the limitless tea and ample supplies of pastry provided for at a shilling a head—were highly critical. If they liked you they applauded with terrible efficiency; if they didn't they adopted very pointed methods of getting you off the stage as quickly as possible.

I am glad to say they liked me from the first, and I have nothing but pleasant memories of my numerous appearances at a type of concert which has long passed into oblivion. I need recall only one incident which stands out in my mind in connection with these Saturday night entertainments in Glasgow. One of the prominent comedians engaged from the south sported a fine astrachan coat. I saw him hang it up in the dressing-room. It fascinated me beyond any other article of male attire I had ever seen. A man who wore a coat like that, I told myself, must be a great artiste. Some day I might have an astrachan coat myself! But surely there was nothing to prevent me having an astrachan collar on my present coat! So with the fee I earned that night I bought a strip of astrachan and got Nance to sew it on to my coat collar. I felt that now I was a real artiste for the first time! When I walked abroad with that coat in Hamilton I had to suffer much chaff and sarcasm. But I stuck to the astrachan collar. It was to me the trademark of an "artiste."

There was a famous old music-hall in Glasgow at this time called the Scotia. It was run by a most competent woman, Mrs. Baylis. She believed in giving local talent a chance. One evening a week several trial "turns" were put on. This was easily the most popular night of the week at the Scotia—the patrons got free rein for their criticisms and for a peculiarly mordant type of humour which I have never come across anywhere else in the world. If a newcomer could "get it across" with the Scotia audiences on a trial night he had the right stuff in him. Several reputations were made in the Scotia on such nights; thousands were blasted irretrievably. Taking advantage of a half-holiday I went up to Glasgow and asked Mrs. Baylis for a trial turn. She looked me up and down and said, "What are ye?" "I'm a comic," I replied. "Well, all I can say is that you don't look like one," was her only comment. Then she turned to her desk and went on working. "I'm really no bad, Mrs. Baylis," I pleaded. "Gie me a chance an' I'll mak' them laugh!" Probably the doleful expression in my words and on my face moved dear old Mrs. Baylis to a reconsideration of my request. At all events she turned around smilingly and remarked, "Laddie, you're makin' me laugh already; come up a fortnight tonight and I'll let ye loose among them for a minute or two. Ye'll maybe be sorry ye were sae persistent!"

When the time came for me to go on the stage at the Scotia I was shaking in every limb. The trial turns preceding mine had all got short shrift. Most of them were "off" in less than half a minute, and those that didn't willingly retire of their own accord were promptly hauled off by the stage manager by the aid of a long crooked stick which he unceremoniously hooked round their necks. The oaths and blasphemy employed by some of the disappointed would-be stars in the wings were only equalled by the riotous mirth of the audience in front. The Boer War was in progress at the time and one of the amateurs, who had had a particularly villainous reception, stopped after the first line of his song, spat three times right into the auditorium, right, centre, and left, and yelled out "I hope the bloody Boers win!" With that he stalked into the safety of the wings muttering and cursing and gnashing his teeth. As it happened, I "got over" pretty well, being allowed to sing two songs with a minimum of interruption and caustic comment. This was really a triumph for any trial run at the Scotia. Before I left Mrs. Baylis came round and congratulated me. "Gang hame an' practise, Harry," she said. "I's gie ye a week's engagement when the winter comes round." I took Mrs. Baylis's advice. I went home and practised harder than ever. And I can truthfully say that I have been practising ever since!

CHAPTER SEVEN

THE LURE OF THE ROAD

SHORTLY after I was married I had seriously to consider the question of my future, whether I was going to remain a miner or take up the stage as a business. Sometimes it happened that I had to leave my work for a few hours or even for a day in order to carry out my professional engagements. As a "local celebrity" I was given quite a lot of latitude by the pit "gaffers" under whom I worked but it was very plain to me that this sort of thing could not go on indefinitely. Nance and I discussed the problem over and over again. So far as she was concerned her last word was always, "Just please yersel', Harry."

I had now got together a fairly extensive repertoire of songs, comic and sentimental, and I felt that if I could only bring myself to take the plunge everything would work out all right. But it was a difficult situation. As a miner I was sure of a good wage; as a comedian my income was by no means certain. I had practically decided to remain in the mines, only accepting an occasional engagement near home, when Fate again took a hand in my destiny.

Resting in front of the fire one evening after a hard day's work at the coal-face, my eye caught an advertisement in the *Evening Citizen*. It read—"Comedian wanted for six weeks' Scottish Tour With Concert Party. Apply So-and-So, Glasgow." I pointed out the advertisement to Nance. We looked at each other.

"What about having a cut at it?" I said.

Again the old phrase, "Just please yersel', Harry!"

Deciding that no great harm could come of at least finding out the particulars I wrote a letter of application there and

82

then. We forgot all about the matter for a week or so but
at the end of that time I received a telegram—the first I had
ever received, by the way—asking me to interview The Kennedys at an address in Glasgow. I found them to be a
husband and wife who were pretty well known as the organ-
izers of concert tours round the smaller Scottish towns.
Their annual summer journey was due to commence in a
few days' time. Would I take the place of a comic who
had let them down at the last minute? The tour had been
planned for fourteen weeks, covering some of the nicest little
towns in the prettiest districts of Scotland. The salary
offered was thirty-five shillings a week. For this I would be
expected to play three turns on the programme every "show"
and also act as baggage-man, bill-inspector, stage-carpenter,
and also check-taker for the cheaper parts of the house. The
Kennedys were careful to point out that this would be a great
chance for a young comedian and they urged me to consider
the pros and cons. Everything was fixed up there and then.

But my head was in a whirl all the way back to Hamilton.
When I told Nance what had happened the tears came into
her eyes. I think we both "grat" a bit that night. It was a
risk, an adventure, a parting of the ways between the coal-
pit and the footlights! For hours after we went to bed
Nance and I talked and talked over this sudden and unexpected change that had come into our lives. When she fell
asleep, wearied and worried, I continued to con over all the
possibilities, whether of success or failure, of the new life
that lay before me. After all, I finally decided, my heart
was really in my singing rather than in the drab, hard, soul-
searing toil and moil of a collier's existence. Besides, if I
failed I could always go back to it! But my mind was made
up—I would do or die!

The tour was due to start at Beith, in Ayrshire, on the
following Monday. I worked right up till mid-day on the
Saturday and then staggered the under-manager by inform-

ing him I had accepted an attractive professional engagement which would prevent me resuming my duties as a
miner. This portentous sentence had occupied my mind for
a long time in the concocting and after I had reeled it off I
felt very proud and independent. The manager looked at me
with a mystified, half-pitying smile.

"Harry, ma lad," he said, "yer a guid miner an' no a bad
wee singer. I'm thinkin' ye'll be back in a week or two wi'
yer tail atween yer legs!"

But he wished me success all the same, adding, wistfully,
that he wished he had the chance himself to see a bit o' God's
green country. We shook hands cordially and parted but as
the "gaffer" turned away he stopped and cried over his shoulder, "If ye come roond Hamilton way, mind an' send me a
free pass for yer concert!"

Nance and I spent all the Sunday together plotting and
planning and dreaming. In the evening we wandered out
the Lanark Road where we had done our courting. We hated
to think of the parting on the morrow and "mony a sigh
an' farewell kiss" were exchanged between us. At nine
o'clock the following morning I caught the train to Beith
where the rest of the concert party were due to arrive later
in the day.

The Kennedys were popular entertainers and the tour
throughout was quite successful. We went all over Ayrshire and Dumfriesshire to begin with and then gravitated
to the Border district and up to the Scottish midlands. I
made three appearances on every programme, singing at least
six songs a night and frequently more if I "got over" well.
Sometimes I did and sometimes I didn't. At the larger
towns, where they had had a chance of hearing other travelling comedians, I was very successful but at certain small
places the people didn't seem to know whether to laugh or
cry. So they did neither—just sat still, listened, and looked
stupidly at me!

"MAN, HARRY, YE'ER TIE'S AYE SQUINT"

My pride got a nasty blow one evening in a village near Berwick-on-Tweed. I was leaving the hall after the show and was feeling rather sad because I had not had, to say the least of it, nearly so good a reception as a third-rate juggler who was one of the artistes. Standing at the foot of the lane leading up to the rear entrance of the hall was a group of "locals" discussing the quality of the entertainment they had just listened to. I heard my name mentioned. Pulling my cap down over my eyes I slowed up my pace anxious to hear what the "fans" were saying about me.

"He's a droll wee deevil that Hairry Lauder craitur—the comic chap that cam' oot sae often," one of the men was saying.

"Tuts, man," sneered a companion, "he's no a real comic at a'—he's the bill-inspector an' he's only thrown into the programme to kill the time! He was in my shop this mornin' beggin' me to show a bill! The wife turned to me when he gaes oot an' says she, 'What's that half-wittit "under-sized" nyacket onywey, Dauvit?'" I didn't wait to hear any more. The tears came into my eyes.

All the same that first concert trip was really an unending joy to me. We covered hundreds and hundreds of miles of Scottish territory which would otherwise have remained a sealed book so far as I was concerned. My passion for my native land was whetted more than ever. I revelled in its scenery, in its people, its customs and traditions. At every new place we pitched our nightly tent, so to speak, I made it my task to inquire into the local history and what great men or women the town or village had produced. I had every opportunity for doing this sort of thing because, as I have already told you, I had to act in the capacities of a veritable Poo Bah—baggage-man, bill-inspector and distributor, stage-carpenter and front-of-the-house man while the people were assembling for the concert.

Immediately on arriving in a new village I had to see the

"props" removed to the concert-hall. After that I set out for
a tour of the main streets carrying with me a huge pile of
leaflets which I distributed to everybody who would accept
one. I had to call on the local billposter who had done our
advertising a few days before, pay his account, and go round
with him handing out free passes for the entertainment to
such shopkeepers who had been kind enough to display our
placards in their windows. After dinner I adjourned to the
hall and superintended the stage fit-up ready for the evening.
Often I had to tackle the whole job myself when no assistance was available. Then home to my lodgings, a cup of
tea, and back to the hall in time for the "early doors." This
was my daily programme. As often as not the company were
up at six o'clock in the morning if the "jump" was a long
one. Apart from travelling and their actual work on the
stage none of the others did anything—all details and odd
jobs were left to the "wee comic" who found himself hard
at it from early morning till late at night, a fourteen- or
sixteen-hour day, and all for thirty-five shillings a week!

But I loved every minute of it. Compared with my old
life as a miner I felt like a bird suddenly liberated from its
cage. It seemed as though some good fairy had waved her
wand over me and had changed all the drabness of life, the
colourlessness of my former existence, into the romance of
travel, the glory of fresh air, sunlight, freedom!

How did I manage on thirty-five shillings a week, you
may ask. Splendidly is my reply. Every week I sent Nance
a postal order for a pound. This left me fifteen shillings for
my own personal expenses. It was more than ample! While
the more prominent "stars" on the programme generally put
up at the local hotels the lesser fry scouted round the town
for cheap lodgings the moment they arrived. In these days
the local stationmaster in most of the Scottish towns and
villages kept a list of householders who were not above taking a nightly boarder. If the stationmaster was not immedi-

ately available there was always the local policeman willing
to oblige with a list of likely domiciles. My plan was to let
all the others have "first cut" at this list; whatever was left
I calculated would be cheapest! And during all the fourteen
weeks of that early tour I seldom paid more than a shilling
for my bed. Occasionally I had to go the length of eighteenpence but against this extravagance I frequently got shelter
for ninepence and sometimes as low as sixpence. All meals
were, of course, extra. But after a week or two on the road
I discovered that it was a paying plan to make a bargain
for bed and breakfast inclusive. I didn't mind, I would
explain to the lady of the house, paying as much as 1/6d
for a good bed and a decent breakfast! Sometimes the door
was shut in my face. As often as not I screwed the landlady
down to a shilling or one and threepence—all in!

Let me admit right off that I slept in some quaint houses
and many queer beds. Only a few weeks ago when I was
playing at the Victoria Palace, London, I got a letter from
a young man now an officer in the Royal Navy asking me,
among other things, if I remembered the night I slept with
his father in Troon, Ayrshire. For a long while I couldn't
make out what the letter referred to but the strings of
memory gradually loosened and I began to remember the
incident which the writer recalled. Thirty-five years ago
I had gone to his mother and asked for a night's lodging.
She explained that her house was full of Glasgow holiday-
makers and that there wasn't a spare bed in the place. But
if I cared to sleep with her husband while she "crept in
aside the twa weans," I could do so and welcome. Of course
I did. The boy who wrote me the letter was not then born
but the fact that Harry Lauder had spent a night in their
house had become a family tradition. The sailor son was
home from Australia and, hearing me sing at the Victoria
Palace, he had written asking if I could verify the story.
I wrote back and assured him that I had had an excellent

sleep with his good father in Troon, but that he snored dreadfully!

Once I had to sleep with a dog! It was at a village in Stirlingshire. There were very few houses in which boarders could be accommodated and at the very last house on the list I was told that it was quite impossible to put me up. I said I would gladly sleep on the floor rather than walk the streets all night. The occupants of the house were a miner and his wife. I told them I was an old miner myself and that I was now a comedian touring with a concert party.

This information caused them to relent a bit and the upshot was that I was shown into a small room and told that I could sleep on the floor with a pillow and a couple of blankets which they would provide. To my astonishment there was quite a nice bed in the corner of the room and on the bed was lying, curled up but with a suspicious glint in its eyes, a lurcher dog. I asked whose bed that was.

"Oh," said the miner, "that's Jock's bed!"

"An' wha's Jock, may I ask?" said I.

"That's him!" was the reply, pointing to the dog. The wife explained that the lurcher was the apple of her husband's eye. He was being trained for a race due to come off in a week or two. He always slept in this bed. But he was a quiet dog and wouldn't disturb me if I didn't disturb him! I felt inclined to suggest that Jock should be made to sleep on the floor and that I should have his bed but the night was cold and wet outside and I deemed it better to cause no unnecessary complications. So my "shake-down" was duly prepared and we all wished each other good-night.

An hour or two later I was startled out of my sleep by Jock licking my face. I was very cold and uncomfortable. But the lurcher was evidently quite friendly inclined. Stretching out my hands I happened to touch his bed. How cozy and warm it felt! So I just slipped into the dog's bed. He jumped in beside me and together we fell sound asleep.

When the landlady came into the room to waken me in the morning she expressed great astonishment at seeing me in the dog's bed and coolly added that Jock was a "funny brute, sair gone in the temper and awfu' gien to bitin' folk, especially strangers!" I was glad to get away from the house without doing anything to spoil "Jock's" good impression of me—his recent bedfellow.

On another occasion I had agreed to pay a shilling for my bed to an old widow woman in a village in Galloway. Before going off to the concert about seven o'clock in the evening she told me that she would just leave the outside door on the latch and that I would find the kettle on the hob if I wanted to make myself a cup of tea after the show. In the course of the concert one of the other artistes told me that he had not yet fixed up any place to sleep in. So I told him he could come with me if he promised to pay ninepence for his share of the accommodation. He readily agreed. My intention was to pay the old lady eighteenpence for the two of us and thus reduce my own personal liability in the matter by threepence!

The two of us went home and made ourselves some tea, both drinking out of the same cup, and eating the remains of a packet of biscuits which I had got from a grocer when I handed him his free pass for the show. Soon we went to bed but were wakened about three o'clock in the morning by a noise as of someone suffocating. After lying in bed for a few minutes debating in low and anxious tones what we should do and advancing all sorts of explanations for the weird sounds from accident to murder I crept out from between the blankets and lighted a stump of candle the while my companion sat up in bed with his hair actually standing on end with terror. It did not take me long to trace the groans and gurglings to a press in the corner of the room.

Darting back to the bedside I said, "My God, Jamie, but there's some dirty work been done here this nicht! We've got mixed up in something dreadful and we'll baith be for it wi' the police in the mornin'."

Meantime the sounds continued worse than ever. At last we decided to investigate further. Taking our courage in both hands we advanced again to the press door and listened carefully. All at once it opened of its own accord and a woman's body rolled on to the floor of the room at our feet. My trembling chum, who was now holding the candle stump, let the flame touch a tender portion of my anatomy. I shrieked; he did the same and so did the "body." The candle fell and went out. I tripped over a chair and went smash full length on the floor, roaring like a bull. The uproar brought several neighbours to the house in their night attire. The explanation of the "mystery" was very simple. The poor old body had only one room and as she did not see why she should lose the shilling I offered for the night's lodgings she had crept into the press intending to doze there for the night and get up silently in the early morning before her lodger was awake. When the press door gave way and she was suddenly thrown into the room, finding two men instead of one, she "kink her senses athegither" and started to shriek the place down!

The rest of the night we spent in a bed provided by one of the sympathetic neighbours and in the morning the old woman got her eighteenpence all the same. Many and many a time have I laughed over the incident of the landlady who tried to sleep in the kitchen press!

It was on this first tour that I had the opportunity of visiting Robert Burns's birthplace at Alloway and also the house wherein he died at Dumfries. Afterwards, in the old bookshop in the square at Dumfries I purchased for tenpence a second-hand volume of his poems and songs. Every minute I had to spare in each busy day I poured over this treasure; the book was my constant companion and my joy. I learned all Rabbie's songs by heart. My favourites were

"O Wert Thou in the Cauld Blast," "Mary Morrison,"
"O A' the Airts the Wind Can Blaw," "Come under My
Pladie," "Corn Rigs," "Bonnie Wee Thing," and "My
Nannie's Awa." But, indeed, every song of Burns which
dealt with love and the lasses, oh, appealed to me tremendously and I remember, in those weeks of my first rapture
for the great bard of Scotland, telling myself over and
over again that some day I would compose a song or two
which would also exalt and glorify the charms of some unknown Mary or Jeannie, or Nell, or Annie. Yes, a Harry
Lauder love-song that would be sung all over the world!

As luck would have it the tour also brought me to the
birthplace of men like Tannahill, the Paisley Poet, and
James Hogg, the Ettrick Shepherd. These men I worshipped
second only to the Immortal Robert himself and I possessed
myself of copies of their books and of every book or pam-
phlet that had ever been written about them. They were my
Heroes of Scottish Song. I was only a poor, uneducated
miner but with what entrancement did I read, over and over
again, the Supreme Wish of Robert Burns—

> —A wish (I mind its power)
> A wish that to my latest hour
> Will strongly heave my breast——
>   That I, for poor auld Scotland's sake
> Some useful plan or book could make
>   Or sing a sang at least.

At that time and for years afterwards I frequently felt
that the stuff I was singing was poor and tawdry and unworthy, but the determination to write a good love-song some
day never quite forsook me. Whether, even yet, I have
succeeded is not for me to say but I would express the wish
that if I am remembered for any of my songs it will be for
such lyrics as "Roamin' In The Gloamin'," "I Love A
Lassie," "Over the Hills to Ardentinny," or my latest and
greatest song, "My Heather Belle."

All too soon for me the Kennedys' tour came to an end
and I found myself back at Hamilton again. I was now, in

my own estimation at least, a fully fledged professional comedian and I never doubted that the engagements would roll in for the illustrious Harry Lauder. As a matter of fact two "inquiries" were waiting for me on my return and as they were both "guinea-and-a-halfers" I felt that the world was really a very cheerful place to live in after all. Nance had actually saved nearly ten pounds from the pound a week I had been sending her.

How she achieved this wonderful record I did not inquire too closely; I suspected that she had spent most of the time with the auld folks, who were only too glad to have her assistance in looking after the children of whom by this time there must have been eight or ten. Altogether the Vallances had fourteen, several of them coming on the scene long after we were married and had a boy of our own, John.

My return to Hamilton was a great event among our family circles and my own pals and admirers. I was regarded as a prodigy; the astrachan coat was worn every day and for a week or two I strolled about the town with a lordly air, thoroughly enjoying the envious looks of my old cronies as they went to and from the pits in their greasy clothes.

Alas, my state of independence was not fated to last long. After I had fulfilled the two engagements which were waiting me the postman religiously passed our door. Nobody seemed to want the services of Harry Lauder, comedian. The money my wife had saved was slowly dwindling away: I was eating the bread of idleness—a terrible thought! At last my mind was made up. I would go back to the pit and give up all hope of ever making a living on the stage. Only too well did I know what such a decision meant in the way of jeers and sneers from the comrades I had left in the mine less than six months ago. But the situation was desperate. There were only two things I could do—sing or cut coal. Evidently nobody wanted to hear me sing. Getting a job at the coal-face presented no difficulty whatever, so I "signed on" with the under-manager who had prophesied so accurately that I would be back with my tail between my legs. He was a kindly man and he, at least, did not rub in the fact that I was a "stickit comic." I cannot say as much for some of the men, and weeks elapsed before they allowed me to forget the fact. There was nothing really bitter about their chaff but it galled me dreadfully. I think I must have expended my rage and mortification on the coal-face for I worked like a galley-slave and made splendid wages—much more, I can assure you, than the fellows who were inclined to laugh at me.

CHAPTER EIGHT

COAL-FACE OR FOOTLIGHTS

So FIRM was my resolution to remain a miner that I actually refused several small concert jobs that were offered to me in places round about Hamilton but I did accept a special engagement or two at the Glasgow Harmonics—the bursts, as they were called. In writing about these unique entertainments earlier in my memoirs I think I said that this name was given to them on account of the prodigious swillings of tea and the capacious bagfuls of pastry with which the audience were regaled.

There was, however, another reason for the name and probably a more likely one. It was the custom of the men, women, and children who made up the audience to retain the paper bags after they had consumed their contents and use them as explosives when they wanted to demonstrate their special approval of the work of any of the artistes. If a singer or a comedian or a juggler or a paper-tearer did not just "get over" the front of the house applauded by hand-clapping, or refrained altogether from appreciation of any kind. On the other hand, any other artiste who appealed to them very much was not only cheered vociferously but the paper bags were blown up and burst with cannon-like effect.

I have heard gun-fire on the Western Front during the war which could not compare for genuine ear-splitting with the din made by the bursting of a thousand paper "pokies" at a Glasgow Saturday-Night tea-fight. For myself I must say I was one of the most popular performers at these functions and it was after a most enthusiastic reception on a December Saturday—every paper bag in the hall went off bang! in my honour as I left the stage—that I felt the old lure of

the stage again taking possession of my soul. On the way
home I tried to fight against it, telling myself that only disappointment, failure and misery would result.

But a letter which awaited me on my return to Hamilton
completely wrecked my balance. It was from the late J. C.
MacDonald, then the leading comedian in Scotland and a
tremendously popular personage throughout the length and
breadth of the land. Here I think I must say a few words
about J. C. MacDonald and the prominent part he played in
shaping my whole future career from this period onwards.
I had heard him frequently on the stage and the concert
platform. He was a fine type of Scotsman, with a good voice
and an altogether remarkable insight into Caledonian character and customs which he made splendid use of in his comic
songs and patter. His stage presence, either in costume or in
ordinary clothes, was most impressive. He had personality.
Added to it he had the unusual faculty of dominating an
audience the moment he stepped from the wings. How I
used to admire his entrance and his exits. The former were
airily defiant; the latter left an atmosphere of graciousness
and good humour all over the house. At the time of which
I write J. C. MacDonald must have been a comparatively
well-off man. He had been King of the Scots comics for
many years. He had toured his own companies under the
name of MacDonald's Merrymakers every summer visiting
only the large cities and towns. The advent of MacDonald's
Merrymakers was a red-letter day at the seaside resorts in
particular. Everywhere he went he was certain of a full
house and a tremendous reception for himself and his company.

Two songs sung by "J.C." stand out specially in my
memory. One was entitled "Sandy Saft a Wee," the story of
a Scotch "Natural" who was not so daft as he was cabbage-
looking. It has often been said in Scotland that I got the
idea for my famous song "The Saftest o' the Family" from

this character-study by MacDonald. That is not so. My "Saftest o' the Family" was inspired by a little Glasgow ragamuffin and the whole treatment of my study is on quite different lines to those of my old friend and patron. I'll tell you later the full story of how I came to write "The Saftest o' the Family."

The other MacDonald effort I refer to was a character song about a Glasgow Irishman who was the champion "cairter" (drayman) of his district. MacDonald made a real work of art out of the character. Complete with whip, "bunnet," sleeved waistcoat, and trousers tucked up with string below the knee he was the Glasgow lorryman to the life. The chorus of the song had a fine swinging lilt to it and I have not the slightest doubt that I have only to recall the words for thousands of elderly Scots to remember the pleasure MacDonald gave them with his rendering of the song. Here they are:

> Woa! Vain. Haud aff Ye! That's Cahoon,
> The buttons on his waistcoat are as big as hauf-a-croon;
> He gets mair pey than a' the ither men
> An' the horse he drives can run awa' wi' fower ton ten!

I have heard great audiences yell this chorus with immense gusto. Like many other comic songs the chorus words of this one seem pretty limp and "fushionless" but I can assure you that MacDonald made a tremendous hit with it. Even today, forty years after, you can hear staid, respectable old men in Scotland humming the tune about the Glesca cairter!

Well, it was from no less a personage than J. C. Mac-Donald himself that the letter came which was waiting for me that Saturday night. It was a kindly letter, setting forth that the writer had never had the pleasure of hearing me but that he had had many good reports of my ability. Would I care to deputise for him during the forthcoming New Year week at Greenock Town Hall? He was not feeling very well but if he could not find a good deputy he would have to turn

'FOU TH' NOO!'

up and do his best. Ten performances; Salary three pounds.
What did I say? Nance and I read the letter several times.
She could see I was "ettling" to accept the offer.

"Just please yoursel', Harry," was again her only observation. So then and there I wrote off thanking the famous
comedian for his kindness and gladly accepting the engagement.

That week at Greenock is a nightmare to me even yet.
The Greenock and Port Glasgow rivetters and engineers
rolled up in their hundreds to the Town Hall at every performance but they came more to make entertainment than
be entertained. Some of the artistes, myself included, had
an exceedingly stormy passage. On the last night of the
week they literally gave us hell; the hissing was so insistent
that I swore a steam-pipe must have burst in the hall. I
have been back in Greenock more than once. But I can't
say I really like the place—when I remember that New Year
week!

At the end of it I crept up to the station with my Gladstone bag and fell into the train limp, broken-hearted and
cursing myself for working instead of having a jolly good
holiday, with my family and friends. The only consolation
was that I had over two pounds in my pocket whereas a holiday would have cost me fully as much—four pounds of a
difference "on a division" as the politicians say. Considering
this aspect of the situation I soon cheered up. Besides, it
was worth being away from Nance for a whole week just
to see the light kindle in her bonnie blue e'en when I took her
in my arms once more. Oh, but she was wonderful in these
days—just as she has always been!

Of course it was back to the pit again after Greenock.
And there I honestly meant to remain. The stage life, I told
myself, was too uncertain and the rewards not sufficient to
tempt a man from the mines where he was always sure of a
living wage. But how easily I fell from these resolves when-

ever the stage beckoned. I hadn't been back at work more than a month when, through the influence of J. C. Mac-Donald, I was offered a month's tour of the Moss and Thornton halls in the north of England finishing up with a couple of weeks at the Scotia and Gaiety, Glasgow.

"Nance," said I, "this is the last chance. If I don't make good now I never will. In any case I can't carry on as I'm doing—a week or two in the pits and a week or two on the stage. It has got to be one or the other. The mine managers won't stand for it. I'm finished as a miner; if I can't be a success as a comic singer I'll find another job above ground and never sing another song as long as I live."

I was as good as my word. I said farewell to the mines forever. Tom, my brother-in-law, brought up my "graith"— my working tools, lamp, etc.—some weeks after I had gone on a tour and he has them to this day. A year or two ago I donned the old clothes and implements to take part in a big charity performance in Manchester on behalf of a mining disaster fund. I was so overcome with emotion at all the circumstances that the tears rolled down my face as I stood in the wings and Tom had to thump me on the back and shake me before I was fit to go on and appeal for money for the wives and bairns of the dead miners. But for the accident of fate, I realized, I might myself have ended my days in one of the tragic happenings that are always part and parcel of the poor miner's existence.

That first music-hall tour was splendid experience for me. It knocked the rough corners off my acting and the very first night or two—I opened at Newcastle by the way—demonstrated one thing to me in most emphatic fashion. I might be a Scotch comedian, and an exceedingly good one in my own estimation, but it was utterly hopeless to break into England with purely Scottish dialect and words and idioms which nobody over the border understood. This important consideration had certainly been weighed up in my mind before coming south. How was it possible, I asked myself, for English people to comprehend Glasgow slang and idiom when other people, in other districts of Scotland, could not make head or tail of it?

Scottish dialect is a most extraordinary thing. I have met Aberdeenshire men and women who spoke a language which was absolutely unintelligible to the stranger from four counties further south. In Dundee the purely local dialect has words, intonations, and meanings which are, for all practical purposes, double-Dutch to the fine clear-speaking folks of Inverness and further north. The Fife man and woman employs words and phrases, and does so in a high head-tone, quite impossible of interpretation by the people of any other district in Scotland. This mixture of dialects prevails in all countries of the world, I suppose, but nowhere is it so pronounced as in Scotland.

Ask anybody the world over—never mind whether low-land Scot or Laplander—this question and see what answer you will get other than a puzzled stare—"Fa fuppit the fite fulpie?" Yet it is perfectly understandable in Aberdeen as, "Who had the cruelty to whip the little white dog?" Or again, "Seenafellafaaffalarrie" easily stands in Dundee for "I have just seen a man fall off a cart," but it is gibberish to any other person than a certain type of quick-speaking Dundonian. Speak about "agin th' waa" outside of Glasgow, or "wabbit" outside of Fifeshire, and you will be using words that are unknown and convey not the glimmerings of a meaning, but which are in daily use in the districts mentioned.

I swear that I myself in the old days have heard Aberdeenians speaking together for long intervals and have been absolutely unable to follow the gist of their conversation.

There is a classic story told about an Aberdeen man who came up to London for a holiday and found himself in Piccadilly about eleven o'clock at night. He was amazed at the coloured advertisements in electric light (Broadway would probably have stopped his breath for good!) and inquired of a newsboy the following:—"Hey loonie, fat's a them reed and fite an blue lichties bobbin oot an in ower 'ere see?" The gamin, polite to start with, begged pawdon, sir, and asked him what he had said the first time. The Aberdonian repeated his question in the same dialect but a bit quicker. Again the newsboy confessed that he was unable to "follow" and would the gentleman repeat his question, speaking "a bit slower, guv'nor?" Once more the northern visitor demanded to know "fat's a them reed and fite and blue lichties bobbinootaninowereresee?" but his temper was becoming shorter by this time and he hurried the last words all together. The newsboy gave him one look of supreme contempt, ejaculated, "Get aht, ye b——y Portugee!" and passed on his way rejoicing.

Remembering all these idiosyncrasies of Scottish dialect I decided that if ever I got a footing in England I would not use words or idioms which would only befog my audience. I would sing my songs in English I determined *but with a Scottish accent.* The result was that I was more successful my first week in Newcastle than any other Scottish artiste who had appeared there. The local manager told me on the Saturday night that a few weeks previously they had had a Scot on the bill and nobody could understand a single word of what he said. Of course he "got the bird" badly. Two or three years later I met the little comedian he had referred to and I turned the conversation to Newcastle, asking him how he had done there. "Terrible!" he admitted. "They yelled me off the —— stage every nicht, Harry. They canna unnerstan' plain English there—naething but broad Geordie!" He went on to explain that he had tried to translate comic Scotch songs into English. This statement intrigued me immensely and I asked him to sing a verse of

one of his songs "translated." He was quite willing to do so
and at once warbled out:

> "My led's a pollisman
> A thumping Highling pollisman
> He gone and join'd the pollis fors
> He was so charmed with work.
> He came from the Highlings
> With a load of potato pilings
> And I'm going to merry him
> On Hogmanay night!"

I almost died laughing at this outlandish nonsense and to
this day when I want to amuse my friends all over the world
I tell them the story of the wee comic who tried to translate
his songs for the benefit of the Tynesiders. From Newcastle
I went on to South Shields and then to the Hartlepools and
Sunderland, etc. My salary for this tour was three pounds
ten shillings. The place on the bill I occupied was a very
humble one; I was either first turn or last and many a night
I played to empty seats.

But those people who did hear me were generous in their
applause. And I made certain that they understood every
word of what I was singing or talking about. That I held,
and still hold, to be the very first aim and object of an
artiste anywhere. The last two weeks of the tour were in
my own city of Glasgow and I was delighted with the receptions given me there. There was a warmth and spontaniety
in the applause of my Glasgow admirers which meant much
in the way of encouragement and determined me to go right
ahead with some new songs and character stuff. I had been
planning while on tour.

I was thoroughly displeased with the material I was
using. My songs were poor even if they were funny. Frankly,
they would have been considered trash had any other person
tried to sing and act them, but I must say, in honesty to
myself, that I presented them with all the power, "pawki-
ness," or dash that I could put into them. I had almost
forgotten that in these days, too, I was a sentimental singer.

I had one ballad which I bought from a Trongate "poet" and
it never failed to get over with the "gods." It was entitled
"You Can't Put an Old Head on the Shoulders of a Child!"
I forget—I don't want to remember—how the verses went
but the chorus, sung to a slow, dirge-like wail, was as
follows :

> Treat them with kindness, don't cause them pain
> Let not passion master you but always play the game
> For children will be children and remember though they're wild
> You cannot put an old head on the shoulders of a che-ild!

The admirable sentiment contained in this last brilliant line
was emphasised and underlined by my throwing out both
hands in an appealing attitude to the audience and getting a
pathetic "break" into my voice. I have no doubt it was a
masterly performance of its type and for its time but I
would not go on any stage in the world today and sing that
awful song for a thousand pounds a night! And I would
do a lot for that amount of money, mind I'm tellin' ye!

Another song I was singing round about this period was
entitled "The Bonnie Wee Man." It was founded on an old
Scottish air—as I am free and ready to confess that many
of my songs were founded—of a very rollicking nature.
Here is a verse and chorus :

> There was a wee man cam' coortin' me
> A bonnie wee man ca'd Tammy McPhee
> And oh but he was a treat to see
> The chappie that cam' to court me.
>
> And oh but he was a fly wee man
> A shy wee man an' a sly wee man
> A regular greasy, citrate magnesie
> Chappie that cam' to woo me.
>
> He lookit sae handsome what dae ye think
> His e'en were blue an' black an' pink
> I'm tellin' ye he was nae sma' drink
> Was the callint that cam' tae coort me.

I realized quite well that such songs as these, while they
passed muster as the stock-in-trade of a three or four pounds
a week comedian would never get me anywhere. The first

of my real song successes was "Tobermory." This was inspired by my seeing a boatload of holiday-makers leave the Greenock pier one night for the West Highlands. There were two working-men from Glasgow on board and one of them kept constantly shouting to his friends ashore what "he and Mackay would do in Tobermory!" The idea was a good one for a song and I worked hard on it while "the iron was hot." The song was a success from the outset but it was a year or two before I had it perfect down to the laughter which consumes me as I try to lay off the patter. This laugh I practised for months until I got it natural and effervescent enough. From the very first night I sang "Tobermory" at a concert near Hamilton it had to remain in my repertoire for years. And I have sung that song ten thousand times in every part of the globe.

The next good song I got was "The Lass o' Killie-crankie." For the germ of the idea and some of the lines I had to thank Sandy Melville, an old Glasgow song-writer who in his time sold hundreds of songs to comedians and straight singers visiting the Music Halls in the West Country. Poor Sandy Melville! He was his own worst enemy. Had he not been so fond of a dram he might have been a successful man in any walk of life. As it was, all he asked of life was to be able to sell an occasional song, recitation, or idea and spend his hours in a wee public-house in the Stockwell of Glasgow. Often and often he came to me either at my home or in the dressing-rooms of the theatres when I became better known. From the depths of a tattered pocket he would produce odd dirty pieces of paper on which he had scribbled a line or two of a song or an idea for a comic situation, or a joke or a story. "Help yersel', Harry," he would say. Nine times out of ten there would be nothing I could use but the tenth time there would be a couplet or a verse which I could work up into something good. Many a sovereign dear old Sandy had from me but I always got good value from him. Sandy Melville was the author of a song which achieved widespread popularity in Scotland and all over the world twenty years ago. At the moment I forget the title of the song but it was an emigrant song and the first verse was:

> They're far, far awa'
> But their hearts are ever true.
> The auld hoose at hame is constant in their view.
> The bonnie bloomin' heather and the hill-taps clad wi' snaw—
> Their hearts are eye in Scotland tho' they're far, far awa'.

Every great contralto vocalist in the land had the song on her list and I myself have heard men and women sing it in all parts of the globe. Poor Sandy Melville!

CHAPTER NINE

I BECOME MY OWN IMPRESARIO

ALMOST simultaneous with the improvement in my repertoire which the songs I have just spoken of represented I
began to get more work than I could tackle and found myself actually compelled on several occasions to refuse engagements. There were forty or fifty letters waiting me
when I came home after that first Moss and Thornton tour
and practically each one contained the offer of an engagement. So I determined to raise my fees. I would accept
nothing less than a guinea and a half and my rail fare! To
my great delight many of the concert promoters gladly
agreed to my terms with the result that my income was
sometimes as high as five and six pounds a week.

Naturally some of the people I had been glad to sing for
a year or two earlier for five shillings and ten shillings a
night were in high dudgeon about Harry Lauder's "swollen
heid" and didn't make any mistake about telling me off
for my greed and rapacity. The secretary of a football club
in Cambuslang with whom I had formerly been on friendly
terms wrote me a very snappy letter in which he demanded
to know if I considered myself an Adelina Patti, finishing
his epistle by saying I would live to regret not coming to
Cam'slang and that he would tell everybody the dirty trick
I had played his club and its annual concert!

In the autumn of 1896 I got an engagement for six
weeks with Mr. Donald Munro's North Concert Party and
this started a friendship which has been one of the great
joys of my life. Donald is a big man in Aberdeenshire today
and is the Provost of Banchory, the lovely Deeside town
which he has always envied. At the time of which I write

105

Donald was in the timber trade—he is still one of the leading men in Britain in the timber business—and had more
than a local reputation as an elocutionist and Scotch reciter.
Having a long vacation every summer he hit upon the idea
of touring a concert party in August and September. He
made many tours before I joined him and long after I left
him and I have a shrewd suspicion that the canny Donal'
made a good lot of siller out of his concerts. In any case
he was able to pay me five pounds a week and also to employ
artistes so well known as Jessie Maclachlan the Scottish
prima donna and Mackenzie Murdoch, the best violinist in
my opinion our country ever produced.

We were a well-varied combination and scored a terrific
series of successes all over the northern and midland towns
of Scotland. At the finish of the tour Donald wanted to
re-engage both Murdoch and myself on increased wages but
we laughed and told him that we had learned a trick worth
two of that—Mac and I had laid our heads together and
resolved to become impresarios on our own. But we had
such a respect and sincere affection for Munro that we assured him we would not touch his territory at all when we
started next summer.

"Besides," I added, "the train fares up here are awfu'
dear; we're goin' to stick around about Glasgow where the
jumps won't be so costly. In fact we may walk from place
to place!"

Donald wished us all the luck in the world and our brief
relationship as master and man, ended there and then. But
our personal friendship has grown stronger with the years.
I wish you all knew Donald Munro! What a big, honest,
grand man he is—as straight as his own back-bone!

I had a very good winter after the Munro Tour finished.
For two weeks on end one busy period I played in a different town or village every night. I put on several new songs
but none of them so good as "Tobermory," or "The Lass

o' Killiecrankie." And I was getting as much as two guineas for my services in the larger towns and cities—fairly on the highway to fame and fortune, I proudly assured myself. No matter how much money I earned Nance was a rare one to "save it up" and, to be candid, I think I gave her encouragement in this laudable enterprise! The result was that by the time spring came round and the dull season for concerts arrived we found ourselves with a bank-book and over £150 to our credit. In fact we went and had a full week's holiday a Rothesay—the first full week we had ever had in our lives together. Just to break the monotony I accepted an engagement while there—and earned the cost of the week's jaunt!

Mackenzie Murdoch and I had several meetings during the early summer and we planned out our first tour. We thought it expedient to stick to the West Country where, we told ourselves, we were best known and where we would be sure to pick up a lot of money. Joyfully we looked forward to the adventure. We were on a dead cert, Mac told me and I told Mac; it was going to be money for nothing. We counted what "Capacity" the halls would hold and calculated the profits down to a shilling or two! "Easy Jack," as my American friends would say! Had we foreseen what our actual experience was going to be we would never have "crawn sae crouse" to use an old Scottish phrase meaning that pride goeth before a fall. When the first proofs of the Lauder-Murdoch Concert Party bill came from the printers we stood admiring them for hours at a time and we even got an old woman to slip one into her window in the Garscube Road, Glasgow, just to see how it looked in passing! Murdoch and I both agreed that it was a "clinker" and that it would pull the people into the local halls until the police would "summons" us for overcrowding.

With piles of these same bills Murdoch and I set out together to cover the towns embraced in the first week of the tour, Kilmarnock, Irvine, Kilwinning, Saltcoats, Troon, and Ayr. We must have personally distributed hundreds of the placards and seen to the actual posting of hundreds more on the boardings and on country fences and the walls of disused buildings.

The tour started on August Bank Holiday, 1898. Our company consisted of Harry Lauder, Scotland's Pride (as a little weekly paper had described me a few weeks previously), Mackenzie Murdoch, the World's Greatest Fiddler, Scott Rae, Caledonia's Popular Tenor, Flora Donaldson, Brilliant Soprano, and Howard, London's Star Ventriloquist. And though I say it myself it was a jolly fine concert-party.

Mac and I agreed to draw five pounds a week each out of the income and the salaries of the other artistes amounted, all told, to less than eight pounds a week. The tour was a ghastly failure. Night after night we played to a mere handful of people—that is, if the free passes be excepted, for there was always a good representation of dead-heads. At the end of the first week Murdoch and I were in the blues. The second and third weeks were a little better and the fourth showed a profit, encouraging me to persevere. But the last two weeks were disastrous. One night we played to thirteen grown-ups and fourteen children and of the twenty-seven in the hall sixteen were there on "paper." But this wasn't the worst. At Stenhousemuir, in Stirlingshire, there were exactly eleven people in the hall and the drawings were one shilling and ninepence! I was so enraged that after my second turn I delivered a speech, roundly rating the inhabitants for not turning up in their hundreds to hear "the finest concert-party that ever toured the British Isles." I finished up by saying that my partner, the illustrious violinist Mackenzie Murdoch and myself, Scotland's Pride, would never again set foot in that God-forsaken village. I might have said a lot more had not the village bill-poster at that moment wakened up in his free seat from a drunken slumber and shouted out, "And a damned good job, too! My account's pey'd and ye can a' gang tae hell!" That particular concert ended abruptly. On the afternoon of the very last day of the tour, Murdoch and I went out for a stroll in the village which we both felt was due to be the Waterloo of our careers as concert-prompters. The place seemed dead and we were both moodily silent. All at once Mac started to laugh.

"Look at this, Harry!" he said and pointed to a placard which appeared to contain the following extraordinary announcement:

Only Appearance of

HARRY
LAUDER

The Audience will join in singing the hymn
"Thank God from Whom All Blessings Flow."

At first, being a bit short-sighted, I thought that this was the work of some enemy but closer investigation revealed the fact that one of our posters had got mixed up with the announcement of a religious service to be held in the village on the Sunday following our concert. We both had a good laugh over the incident but behind our merriment was the unspoken idea that the mixing up of the bills was an omen full of evil for our future!

Altogether Murdoch and I lost a hundred pounds each on the tour, returning to Glasgow sadder but wiser men. When I wrote and told Donald Munro of our lamentable failure he replied with a very kindly letter telling us not to be discouraged. He had had the same experience to begin with but this year, even without the support of two great artistes like Lauder and Murdoch, he had cleared quite a decent amount of money! "Try, try, try again, Harry, my lad," he finished up.

As a matter of fact our next venture the following summer, taking a different lot of towns and spending far more money in advertising, got back all that we had lost on the first tour, besides the five pounds a week we again credited ourselves with out of the drawings. Both Mac and I were beginning to be much better known; at some of the towns we visited we had full houses and these places were marked down for concentrated attack the following year.

I have many delightful recollections of the half-dozen tours carried out by the Lauder-Murdoch Concert parties. As I have told you the second of these more than paid its way while the third and fourth were what I should describe as "most gratifying" from a financial standpoint. As a matter of fact I think our third and fourth ventures must have earned for each of us something like six hundred pounds. It was not at all unusual for us to pull forty, fifty, or sixty pounds into the house at some of the larger centres, especially the more popular seaside resorts, while in cities like Edinburgh, Dundee, and Aberdeen I have known us draw over a hundred pounds at a performance. Mackenzie, like myself, had known poverty and hard times and the gradual crescendo of success was as great a joy to him as it certainly was to me.

I was secretary and treasurer in the first year or two of our association. The first of these two posts did not give me a great deal of worry but I carried out my duties as treasurer with meticulous care! I was generally down at the hall very early in the evening and gave the local "stewards," or checkers minute instructions as to their duties and the importance of making sure that nobody got in for nothing! They used to say in London long ago that Sir Henry Irving's mannerism of nodding his head while declaiming his parts was actually his method of counting up the number of people in the house. Sir Henry, so the tale goes, could always tell to a fiver what the drawings ought to be

"THE SAFTEST O' THE FAMILY"

on any particular night. That's nothing! I became so
proficient in estimating the drawings at our concerts that
I could tell to within a shilling or two, immediately I went
on the stage, what my own "rake-off" was going to be after
the salaries and expenses had been accounted for! Later my
brother-in-law Tom Vallance joined up with us as general
manager and ultimately relieved me of the treasureship but
before his advent either Mac or myself carried all the money
to our lodgings. Here we counted it over and over again,
putting the paper money in one heap, the half-crowns in
another, the two-shilling pieces in another and so on down
to the threepenny bits. That to me, let me be perfectly honest
about it, was the finest part of the evening's work! The
first time we took twenty pounds in an evening Murdoch
and I sat up the greater part of the night; we were so excited
that neither of us could sleep. Gaspard, the miser, had nothing on us that night. We would, singly or together, certainly
have murdered any person who attempted to rob us before
we had time to get the money safely in the bank next
morning.

Writing of this sort of thing reminds me of an amusing
incident which happened one evening in Glasgow. We had
given a concert in a village some miles on the north side of
that city and had time, the other members of the company
included, to catch the train for Glasgow soon after the show.
We seldom got home even for a night after the tours started
and we were all glad of the opportunity to do so seeing we
were playing so near our homes. Nance and I by this time
had removed from Hamilton and were living in a flat in
Dundas Street on the south side of Glasgow.

Arrived at Buchanan Street Station we all said good-
night and I made for the nearest cab-rank: I had the money
taken at the doors of the concert in a little leather bag and
it behooved me to take no risks in getting the cash safely
home. I must have fallen asleep because the first thing I

remember was the old horse "cabbie" opening the door of the vehicle and announcing "Dundas Street, sir!" Out I jumped, paid the fare, and ran upstairs. Nance had not expected me, and was in bed, so I just pulled off my clothes and was on the point of turning out the kitchen gas when I remembered I had left the leather bag in the cab.

I gasped. I recollected that there was neary twelve pounds in the bag. I went all shaky and cold sweaty! But in money matters I have always had the reputation of being a man of action. In any event I was that night. Seizing my trousers I made for the door, not even pausing to answer my wife's agonized query as to "what ailed me." At the foot of the stone stairs I pulled on my trousers and dashed off in the direction at which I had hired the cab. A few pedestrians abroad—it was now about one in the morning—thought I was mad. And two policemen tried to stop me. But I "juked" them both and never stopped until I arrived at Buchanan Street. There, alone in the rank, stood the very cab which had driven me home and there, on the dicky seat was the driver, now fast asleep.

"You're the man!" I yelled as I jumped up on the dicky beside him. Thus suddenly awakened from his slumbers and seeing a strange apparition in a state of wild undress appear from nowhere, the cabman let out an ear-splitting yell—and promptly fell off the cab on the other side. I was after him in an instant and we rolled all over the stance, the unfortunate cabman, thinking he was dealing with a lunatic, hoarsely roaring "Help! Murder! Police!"

By and by a couple of policemen came running up. Explanations followed. The upshot was that one of the officers of the law opened the cab door—and brought out the missing bag intact with the precious drawings. I had to give the aggrieved cabman five shillings for assaulting him and the "coppers" a shilling each for a drink. Next day I narrated my midnight adventures to Murdoch and suggested that

the "expenses" should come off the firm as a whole. This
he stoutly objected to, insisting that I was solely to blame
for my criminally culpable handling of the money. I had
to bear the brunt myself. But the incident was a lesson to
me; from that day to this I have never left a bagful of
money anywhere—not even a threepenny bit!

During these concert tours we covered practically every
large village and town in Scotland from the Solway Firth
to John o' Groats, with occasional excursions into the north
of England. We had many amusing experiences but if I
were going to recount the complete history of the Lauder-
Murdoch concert companies it would require a book to itself
and would, after all, only interest Scottish people. But one
or two stories occur to me as worth telling. My first visit
to St. Andrews is brought vividly back to my mind as I
write because I have just been reading about Bobby Jones's
astounding triumph in the British Open Golf Championship.
Surely Bobby must be the greatest player that ever hit a golf
ball plumb up the centre! The next time I am in Atlantic
City I am going to give him a signed post-card of myself!
And perhaps he'll give me a golf club in exchange!

Well, Mac and I, having a few hours to spare at St.
Andrews decided that we must have a game of golf. We
each borrowed a couple of rusty old clubs from the son of
the landlady and as I had found a handful of old gutta
balls in a drawer in my room we deemed our equipment
complete. So down we strolled to the first tee. There were
several couples waiting to go off. As each successive pair
hit their balls resounding whacks Murdoch turned to me and
said, "This game looks dead easy, Harry—just wasting a
good walk!" When our turn came I went forward to the
teeing-ground, took two or three handfuls of sand out of the
box and proceeded to make a mound like a pyramid on the
top of which I carefully placed a very dirty and debauched
gutta ball. The man in the starter's box watched my oper-

ations with a cold, threatening eye and just as I went up for my first stroke he demanded to know if I had paid my green fee.

"What's that?" I asked. I had never heard of green fees.

"A shilling each," was the snappy reply. "And you can't start off unless you've got a ticket!"

This information immediately cooled our ardour for golf but we decided to go through with it even at this colossal expense. I didn't have a shilling on me. Twopence was all I could muster but Mac had some money and paid for the two of us. So up again I went to my pyramid. Taking the biggest of the two clubs with which I was armed I "waggled" it as I had seen the other golfers do at the same time trying to recall the precepts I had imbibed when I was myself a caddie on Mŭsselburgh links many years before. But again a stern voice exclaimed:

"You canna play an iron aff the first tee!"

I thought the man in the box was having a joke with me so I winked at him and said, "Oh, yes, I can—just you watch this!" With that I swiped at the ball. There was a sudden sandstorm and my ball whizzed past the starter's head right into his box. There were yells of laughter from a group of caddies hanging around and even old Greig himself—starter at St. Andrews for countless years and a famous character the world over—could not refrain from joining in the merriment. But he was adamant against our playing irons off the first tee. So he came out of his box— evidently the most dangerous place with me in the vicinity —pitched my ball fifty yards down the course and ordered us off the teeing ground, adding,

"Ye've paid yer green-fees an' I canna stop ye frae the use o' the coorse (much as I wad like tae) but ye can sclaff awa' frae doon-by there." He pointed to where he had flung my ball. Mac and I decided to accept his advice. But we only played one hole. Less than that, as a matter of fact,

for I put my fifteenth shot into the Swilcan Burn and fell
headlong into the mud in a vain effort to retrieve it. That
was enough for me; we went home to the "digs" firm in
our conviction that the game was completely overrated besides being far too dear! (I would like to add that I have
improved considerably since then, that I carry my clubs with
me all over the globe and that nothing on this terrestrial
sphere gives me half so much genuine pleasure as an occasional "bogey" and a still more occasional "birdie"!)

My fiddler partner and I always tried to find rooms
together wherever we went. Apart from being good friends
we thoroughly enjoyed, as I have already hinted, the sensation of counting up the "takings" after each concert. But
occasionally circumstances compelled us to be separated.
Once at Forfar I found solitary accommodation with a
widow-woman who was the most superstitious person I had
ever met in my life. She was worse than my own mother
who, after all, simply believed in second sight, signs, portents, and the like. But this landlady in Forfar went further.
She believed in ghosts, supernatural happenings, visitations
from evil spirits, death warnings, and all the other adjuncts
of the mysterious beyond. I hadn't been in her house ten
minutes when she had me quite "goosey" by her tales, weird
and impossible as they were. On my return from the Reid
Hall after the performance she started again something after
this fashion:

"Ye ken, Maister Lauder, I'm daein' wrang by haein'
ye in this hoose an' I shouldna wonder if something dreadfu'
happens either tae you or tae me! The last time I had a
coupla actors livin' wi' me we had a visit frae the Bad
Anes. Declare tae God! An' when the folks o' the plaicie
(Forfar is known far and near as "the plaicie") winna believe what I tell them I jist bring them into this verra room
and ask them tae look up at the ceilin'. There, dae ye see

onything yerself?" I looked up and sure enough I could detect strange black markings which had only been partially obliterated by a new coating of white-wash. "They look to me like feet-marks," said I trying to laugh the thing off. But the landlady's swift and entire agreement with my diagnosis completely upset me and gave me a cold feeling down the spine. "Feetmarks, says you"—and she was off again full tilt—"Aye, an' naething else but! Hoo did they come there? Fleas can walk on a ceilin' but nae livin' body can dae it. But the deid can walk upside doon an' them marks yer lookin' at this meenit were made by an ill speerit.

"I'll tell ye the story," she continued. "Twa or three months ago I took in as lodgers a Glesca man caa'd Wee Jakie an' his chum. They were traevellin' wi' a concert party jist as ye are yersel' and they had this identical room for three nichts. On the last nicht, aboot five o'clock in the mornin', they let oot sic yells an' skirls that I was waukened frae ma sleep an' cam' tae see fat a' the stushie was aboot. Wad ye credit it, Maister Lauder, but they swore somebody was walkin' on the ceilin' upside doon. 'Are ye drunk or daft,' says I to them, gey sharp-like, but by this time they had lichtit a caunle an' were starin' up at the roof wi' their e'en stickin' oot o' their heids like bools. Fan I followed their example an' keekit up I was knockit a' ditthirie for I declare tae God the ceilin' was covered ower wi' feet marks. At aince I kent what it meant—it was a veesitation for haein' play-actors under ma roof. So I ordered them tae the door there an' then, no stoppin' even tae chairge for their bed and board. I only hope tae God that naething like that happens this nicht." And she left me.

Did I pass a peaceful evening in that room? I did not. I lay awake most of the night and when I did "dover ower" it was generally to jump up in bed with a violent start and listen for the slightest sound above me. I was up very early, paid my bill and cleared out of the haunted house. In the train going to Brechin an hour or two later, I recounted my experience to Murdoch. He started to laugh. "Oh," said he, "that's an old trick of the travelling acrobats in Scotland for getting free lodgings." He went on to explain that one of a couple living in the same room together blackens his feet at the fireplace, gets on his chum's shoulders upside down and so covers the ceiling with foot-prints. Then, after a good sleep, they scream the house down and in the consternation and excitement which follows they make their escape without paying, leaving the poor land-lady overcome with horror and dismay at the thought that her domicile has been marked down by the Evil One! All the company had a fine laugh at my expense. But no one can say that I have ever objected to anybody having *that* at my expense!

We once struck Kilmarnock during the week of an agricultural show and we had the utmost difficulty in getting accommodation. Murdoch and I went all over the town asking for a double bed, or even a shake-down. "I've slept with a dog before now, Mac," I told my companion, "but I wouldn't be surprised if I had to sleep wi' a coo or a pig tonight!" However, just as we were giving up hope a lady householder promised to put us up somehow. She would think over the problem and be ready for us when we returned late in the evening.

Right enough, when we came home from the concert she ushered us into a small room with a bed made up in the corner. By the uncertain light of a tallow candle we undressed and slipped into bed and as we were both very tired we soon fell asleep. By and by I was awakened by a persistent drip of water falling on my neck. Mac also wakened and complained that the roof was letting the rain in. Jumping up in bed with the intention of getting out and investigating, my head came in contact with a loose something swing-

ing about. Without pausing to consider I gave the thing a
pull whereupon both of us were drenched through and
through with a downpour of water which seemed to come
from the roof right above our heads. The landlady had made
us up a bed on the bath and the cord I pulled controlled the
spray four feet above the pillows.

Many and many a happy hour Mackenzie Murdoch and
I spent together on our Scottish tours. After the first year
or two we were established successes and as Tom Vallance
had relieved us of all the routine work we had lots of time
to improve our golf, to learn to fish, shoot, and sail, all of
which we did together. For my part, too, I had time to con-
centrate on new numbers and whenever I hit upon an idea
Mac was always willing to set my tunes to proper music.
He "took down" the melodies of many of the songs I am
still singing and he orchestrated quite a number of them. He
was a great violinist and a fine musician. Compared with
men like Kreisler and Heifitz a girl like Erica Morini, I
suppose he would not have ranked highly but he had the soul
of Scottish fiddle music in him and I have never yet heard a
violinist who could compare with him in his interpretation
of our haunting national airs. If I was sad Mac and his
fiddle could always make me glad; if I was cheery and
blythesome Mac and his fiddle could make me dance for
very joy.

Now he is dead. When the news of his passing reached
me several years ago in New Zealand I had to lie down on
my bed in the hotel and "Greet ma e'en oot." Murdoch never
quite forgave me for parting company with him in our Scottish tours but the fault was not mine—my English engagements became so numerous and, speaking for that time, so
profitable, that I simply had to resign from the Lauder-
Murdoch combination. Poor Mackenzie could not get anybody to take my place and for many years afterwards had
difficulty in earning the income to which his great talents

entitled him. If there is a celestial orchestra in the Happy Land I have no doubt my old friend Murdoch is drawing golden melody from his fiddle-strings and thus cheering the hearts and putting "mettle in the heels" of all true Scots who have gone hence!

CHAPTER TEN

A SOVEREIGN FOR PUBLICITY ONLY

In between the Scottish tours I was kept fairly busy with individual concert engagements and with frequent music-hall bookings over the border. A really great success at Birkenhead under the management of my very dear friend, Dennis Clarke (a white man in the variety business if ever there was one) set simmering in my mind the notion to try my luck a bit further south—as far as London, I told myself. In Liverpool, Birkenhead, Newcastle, Carlisle, and elsewhere in the north of England I had proved that I could get my material and my personality across the footlights and I began to see no reason why I shouldn't have a cut at the metropolitan stage.

I was the more encouraged to do this by hearing from time to time at the Empire, Glasgow, some of the more pre-eminent of the London stars of the day. I went specially to the Empire and listened to men like George Leybourne, Harry Randall, James Fawn, George Lashwood, and Gus Elen. But none of these stirred my artistic soul to its depths. They were all clever and talented in their own spheres. They were probably worth all the money they were drawing although, to be perfectly frank, I had my doubts on this score.

Then one Monday evening I was in Glasgow fixing up a concert or two with J. C. MacDonald when he said to me:

"Harry, the one and only Dan Leno is at the Empire this week. Why not go down and have a look at him? Personally," added J. C., "I admire the little man immensely but he is the type you can only stand once or twice in a season—at least that is how he appeals to me."

An hour later I was sitting in the pit of the Empire waiting for Dan Leno, the idol of London, to come on the
stage. I had eyes and ears for nobody else on the bill and
when the wonderful little Dan rolled on with his "Shop-
walker" song I watched every movement, every twist of the
face, every raising and lowering of his eyelids, and I followed as best I could his quick Cockney patter. Immediately
Leno's turn was over I left the building. Going straight
home I said to Nance, "I've a fortnight 'out', Nance, and I'm
off to London tomorrow. If Dan Leno can get a hundred
pounds a week for singing London songs in Glasgow I
can get at least twenty for singing Scotch comic songs in
London. He's a good artiste but I am equally as good in
my own line."

"Far better, Harry, and I've never seen Dan Leno!" was
my wife's reply. She was always like that, bless her! She
offered no objections to my adventurous trip!

Next morning, the nineteenth of March, 1900, I packed
my "props" into two Gladstone bags, took twenty pounds
of golden sovereigns from the "stocking" we kept in a secret-
spot beneath the kitchen bed, kissed Nance half a dozen
times, and set off to the Central Station, booking there a
third-class single ticket for London. Not a soul I knew
saw me off. I might have been a thief slinking out of Glasgow for the south. But a thief, anxious not to arouse attention by the eccentricity of his personal adornment, would
not have been dressed as I was!

So far as I can remember I wore a shepherd-tartar pair
of trousers above a pair of yellow spats and brown boots, a
coloured waistcoat and a black frock coat. A standing-up
collar, with very large square peaks, and a black-and-green
tie completed, along with a tile hat which did not fit me
very well, a *tout ensemble* which I have no doubt whatever I
regarded as slap up-to-date and calculated to give agents and
others the impression of a very prosperous, perfectly dressed

comedian in mufti. Over my arm I carried the coat with the astrachan collar. Any man of my size and build walking down the Strand or Broadway today dressed as I was the night I struck London for the first time would be mobbed or arrested for holding up the traffic.

The first evening I spent at a cheap hotel in the Euston Road. My bed and breakfast cost three and sixpence—a lot more than I had been in the habit of paying while on tour in Scotland and I resolved that I would have to economize in other directions. So I walked all the way down to Cadle's Agency. This firm had given me some "dates" in the provinces and I felt sure they would be able to get me a show in London. But the head of this firm—I forget his name at the moment—only smiled pityingly when I said that I wanted to get work as a Scotch comedian in one or other of the big West End Halls.

"Harry, my boy," he said, "you haven't an earthly. We have had one or two of your kidney down here before and they have all been dead failures. If you have any money saved up for this trip get away back again before you do it all in!"

This was a most disheartening start. But there were other agents in London, hundreds of them, and I resolved to call on every blessed one of them before I caved in. Late that afternoon I met an old variety agent named Walter Munroe whom I had met in Glasgow. I offered to buy him a refreshment. Like all good professionals he accepted with alacrity and I could see he was most powerfully impressed by the fact that I paid for it with a golden sovereign. Walter took me round several offices but with no result— the agents were all averse to handling the unlucrative business of an unknown Scottish comedian. Late in the afternoon we were walking rather mournfully along the Strand when we ran into Mr. Tom Tinsley, the manager of a little hall known as "Gatti's In The Road." The "Road" referred

BY HENRY OSPOVAT   HARRY LAUDER

AS OSPOVAT SAW ME.   THE CLEVEREST BUT UNKINDEST CARICATURE OF ME EVER PUBLISHED

to was the direct thoroughfare leading south from Westminster Bridge. Tinsley was the first actual manager I met
in London. We adjourned to a public-house and again I
"flashed" a sovereign for publicity purposes. Once more it
had a good effect, Tinsley opening his eyes in palpable
amazement at a Scots "comic" being in such affluence. But
whenever I mentioned that I was looking for a job his
geniality dried up on the spot.

"It's no good, me lad," he assured me. "My patrons at
the "road" would eat me alive if I put you on. I tried a Scot
last year and he had to fly for his life. You're in a foreign
country and the sooner you realize it the better!" Tom had
another drink at my expense and left us but before taking
his departure he noted my "town address" (I had fixed up
a third-floor room in the Lambeth Road at fifteen shillings a
week) and said he would let me know if anything fell out
of his bill at any time within the next week or two. Walter
Munroe took me to several more agencies but we met with
the same reception at them all. "Luv-a-duck, 'Arry," said
Walter Munroe in his most lugubrious tones, "it ain't no
bleedin' good. You ain't wanted up 'ere and that seems the
finish!" And then Walter went his way.

I spent a very cheerless night in my back-third at the
Lambeth Road but was up bright and early tackling more
agents and more managers. I must have walked ten or
twelve miles in that weary search for work. But everywhere
the result was nil—a blank wall of discouragement. When
I got home I asked the landlady—"Any letters, messages or
telegrams?" Had I stopped for a minute to consider I
would never have put so stupid a question for it was a
million to one against any communications awaiting me.
My wife did not know of my address in London yet and
Tom Tinsley was the only person who had taken a note of
it. To my amazement the landlady replied, "Yes, there's a
telegram up in your room!" I dashed upstairs two steps

at a time—had my legs been longer than they are I would have tackled three—rushed into the room and there, sure enough, was a telegram addressed Harry Lauder, Comedian. It read as follows:

> One of my turns ill. Can you deputize at ten o'clock tonight? Reply at once—Tinsley, Gatti's.

Inside two minutes I was in a grocer's shop near by appealing for the use of his telephone. I was so excited that the grocer was constrained to ask me if anybody was dead. "No," said I, "but I've just got my first London job an' it's awfu' important to me!"

"That's the worst of you Scotties," dryly observed the grocer. "You always take your work too d——d seriously. But you'll find the 'phone round the end of the counter there." Tinsley was in his office. I assured him that I would be on hand in good time the same evening and I thanked him profusely for keeping his promise. From the grocer who had been so kind to me in the matter of the 'phone I bought a fivepenny tin of salmon and went home and ate the lot to the accompaniment of a pot of tea and some bread and butter. Feeling pretty chirpy after the repast I began to debate within myself what songs I would sing to the hard-baked lot of Londoners whom I would have to face that night at Gatti's-In-The-Road.

I decided to risk everything on "Tobermory." It was easily the best song in my armour at that time from the point of view of spontaneous humour and "swing." Remember also that I had been singing the number for two or three years in Scotland and in the northern towns of England with really great success. I had the song, word and action, perfect. The value of every phrase, each movement of hand, eye, or limb, the intonation of the laugh, even, as I tell how, "the next time I see McKay he has his arms roon' the neck o' a bottle" had all been studied a hundred times. Yes, if I

was to make good in London it would be my "Tobermory"—
of that I had no doubt in my own mind. If the audience
liked it I would follow up with "The Lass o' Killiecrankie,"
another rollicking song with a good air. And, in the event of
them wanting more, well, I would sing "Calligan," the Irish
character song which I had recently tried out in the north
and the tune of which had already been put on to the barrel-
organs of the country. So you see I did not at all anticipate
failure. But I had made up my mind, all the same, to go
back to Scotland the next day if my "extra turn" at Gatti's
proved a wash-out. Again it was a case of do or die.

I was in the dressing-room an hour and a half before I
was due to go on the stage. I took immense pains with my
make-up. When it was finished and I was ready for my
call I found I had fully half-an-hour to wait. It was dreadful. I couldn't sit, I couldn't stand still; my nerves and
emotions were in a state of tempest. My memory of what
happened in the next hour is completely blurred. But I have
a hazy recollection of dashing on the stage, my crook stick
thumping the floor to give the orchestra the correct time—an
almost unconscious habit to which I have been prone for
many years—of starting my first song in dead silence before
a rather sparse audience, of suddenly hearing a snigger or
two all over the house, and of finishing "Tobermory" amid
an outburst of applause. Down came the curtain. Evidently
the stage manager was under the impression that one number
was quite enough for an extra turn. But the applause and
laughter continued. "Can you give 'em something else, young
Scottie What's Yer Name?" asked the s.m. "Yes, number
four in my music-books—'Killiecrankie!'" I excitedly replied. "Kill a What?" asked the stage manager. "Never
mind," I replied, rapidly changing in the wings while we
were speaking. "Ye'll ken a' aboot it when I've finished."

"The Lass" went even better than "Tobermory." The
audience went mad over the unknown Scot who was making

them laugh and they raised the roof for another song. "Calligan, Call Again" left them still unsatisfied but I had taken up far more time than the programme permitted and the only thing left for me to do was to go on and make a speech of thanks. I assured the audience that although this had been my first appearance in London it would not be my last. My name, I told them, was Harry Lauder, and I asked them to come and hear me whenever they saw the name on a music-hall bill in London.

"Sure we shall, 'Arry," shouted a cockney voice from the fourth row of stalls. "You've made my ol' woman 'ere laugh for the first time since I married 'er!"

This sally put the house into a fit of merriment and I made my exit from the stage the most successful extra turn that ever descended on London from the fastnesses of Caledonia, stern and wild.

Old Tom Tinsley was waiting for me "off" and promptly booked me for the rest of the week—salary three pounds ten shillings! He was delighted with my success and assured me that I was a "made man." All the agents would be down to see my act before the week was out. "And don't sign up for a penny less than five pounds a week, 'Arry! But I must 'ave you for as long as I like at my own terms!" Later I burst another of my store of golden sovereigns on "drinks all round!" Lest there should be any doubts on the veracity of this story I would point out that I was very excited—in fact I must have lost my head for the time being!

The manager was perfectly right about the agents. They turned up at Gatti's not in single spies but in battalions. They pulled out sheafs of contracts all of which I signed gladly without even discussing terms. This is another statement which folks all over the world will have difficulty in believing. Yet I assure them that it is quite true. I was so bewildered by my instantaneous success that my main thought was work rather than money. Vaguely I hoped that

the latter would follow the former but I was as yet too
lacking in shrewdness to make good bargains. The result
of my impetuosity to sign these early contracts was that I
found myself tied up with London managements for years
ahead at salaries which were simply ridiculous in view of
my drawing capacity. However, this is a sore point with me
and always will be and as I shall have occasion to refer to
it again later we will let it drop for the moment!

Tinsley wanted me to stay on at Gatti's for an indefinite
period. He seemed to take it for granted that I would do
so. And I remember with what a feeling of personal importance I told him that this was impossible—I had to go
to Nottingham to fulfill a contract made many months ago.
My first week in London, therefore, was not the start of
a long metropolitan success. That was to come some months
later when I returned and began to play three halls a night.

It was then that the press came in to consolidate the reputation I was rapidly building up all over London. While I
have always been grateful for any kind thing that is said
about my work in the newspapers I must confess that I have
never kept a press "notice" in all my life. Of all the tens
of thousands of columns that have been written about me and
my stage life by the journalists of the world I am certain
I have not kept more than half-a-dozen "cuttings" and these
have been retained because they made me laugh. So that I
am unable, even if I wished, to give you any indication of
the truly wonderful manner in which the London press
boomed me in these early days.

Looking back on them now it seems to me that half my
time was taken up in being interviewed by newspaper men
and being photographed in a hundred different costumes and
attitudes so that editors could illustrate the articles. This
was, of course, very fine publicity for me. But it was
nothing compared to the publicity I received in later years
by the broods of tales and stories circulated about my per-

sonal characteristics in acquiring and husbanding "the baw-
bees"! At first I resented them, then I tolerated them, afterwards I began to invent them myself and encouraged other
people to invent them. They made up a battery of the very
finest free advertisements any stage personality could have
wished for! Yes, all the "Harry Lauder stories" that have
winged their way round the globe during the past thirty
years have only had the effect of putting more siller into my
pouch. Indeed, if I go for a week or two without hearing
a new one, or an old one revarnished, I think there must be
something wrong with my unpaid publicity staff.

But I am wandering, as many of the old Scottish ministers used to do when they became all heated up with their
pulpit fervour. Times and customs in the variety world of
London have changed since the days I "worked" three and
four halls a night for seven pounds a "turn." Nowadays it is
the exception for an accepted "star" to play more than one
house. Twenty years ago, however, every leading artiste
made one West-end appearance per night and filled in the
rest of the evening by visiting two, three, or even four
suburban halls.

Before the days of motor-cars the "top-liner" had a
privately hired cab or two-horse brougham to take him or
her to the different places of entertainment. It was often
touch and go as to whether the driver could make the grade,
as my American friends say, between halls widely separated,
and often an earlier "turn" had to hold the fort until the
belated arrival of the star. Sometimes the latter did not
arrive at all but this did not happen often—a tribute to the
driving capacities of the old London cabbies. When I bought
my first motor-car, a small coupe driven by an engine that
"chugged" like a locomotive, Tom was able to take me all
over London and its suburbs without ever missing a turn
by more than a minute or two.

We often played four halls a night, two of them twice

"I LOVE A LASSIE".
Cartoon by Harmony

"TOBERMORY".
Cartoon by Harmony

where the double programme system had been introduced. Every policeman in Greater London knew my little car and I think they must have loved Tom, for they allowed him to do the most daring things in the way of traffic-dodging, cutting-in, and stealing a yard or two of road wherever possible. Working at this pressure meant leaving home—Nance had come up to London from Glasgow and we were now living in a villa at Tooting—soon after six o'clock and not getting back until long after midnight. But it meant that even in my poorest weeks I was earning from twenty to thirty pounds a week—a fortune as that seemed to me in those far-off days. All the same it did not take me long to realize that I had made some shocking bad contracts with the London managers and proprietors.

My singing and my songs had taken the town by storm. I was received everywhere with tremendous enthusiasm; I never played to anything but capacity. Halls in the various districts such as Poplar, Shoreditch, Crouch End, Islington, Willesden, Mile End, Hackney, etc., which might have been doing bad business for weeks before suddenly found their doors besieged when my name was on the bills. My success was beyond doubt or cavil, as I once heard a London lawyer put it. I always gave of the very best that was in me. My nightly arrival at the stage doors was an event and my departure a triumph, with cheering mobs of admirers yelling all sorts of good wishes and congratulations.

At the old Tivoli, in the Strand, I definitely established myself as one of London's favourites. This was a very small hall, as variety theatres go nowadays, but its programmes were the best of their kind in the world. It was the home and haunt of the young-man-about-town and a London trip by a provincial would have been considered a complete failure did it not embrace several visits to the "Tiv"! Engagements at the Tivoli were not given for a week but for a month, six weeks and two months if you were a leading

artiste. And as many as ten, twelve or fifteen of the world's
best performers were often grouped together on one Tivoli
bill.

The first time I played the old "Tiv" was a memorable
night in my London career. The people wouldn't let me leave
the stage until I had sung every song in my repertoire, this
much to the disgust of several famous artistes who were due
to follow me. Afterwards the management became wise and
I was generally last turn, or very near it. This kept the
house together until my arrival, and, I suspect, was much to
the good of the bars! These were the hey-days—or nights—
of London variety. They have gone forever, I am afraid.

I have seen Tivoli bills which included, in one long list,
such names as R. G. Knowles, George Robey, Wilkie Bard,
Harry Fragson, Marie Lloyd, Vesta Victoria, Little Tich,
Harry Tate, Dan Leno, Paul Cinquvalli, and some of the
best straight singers and actors of the day. There was only
one dressing-room, presided over for many years by a pale-
faced man called Ted and the genial manner in which he
handled his nightly collection of temperamental "stars"
always won my unstinted admiration. Ted was one of my
greatest admirers and fans. One night a red-nosed comedian
came off the stage in silence, walked into the dressing-room
and complained bitterly about the audience being either
asleep or dead.

"Oh, no, Joe," said Ted, just then assisting Tom to get
me ready, "they're waitin for 'Arry, 'ere!"

This enraged the other so much that he lifted a boot and
threw it at the dresser's head, missing it by inches. On the
whole, however, the other artistes appearing on the Tivoli
programmes with me were warm in their appreciation of
my drawing-powers. Some of them openly warned me that
my amazing popularity wouldn't last and urged me to sting
the managements for as much money as I could get away
with while my vogue was strong "in front."

It was in my early days at the Tivoli, and, later, at the Pavilion and other West-end halls that I began fully to realize how precipitate I had been in signing up for periods of years at salaries out of all proportion to my actual worth from a proprietor's point of view. But as time went on a silver lining, aye, a golden one, appeared beyond the clouds of my financial missed markets. A wonderful pantomime engagement in Glasgow came along. And America began to beckon me.

CHAPTER ELEVEN

PANTOMIME

THE Christmas Pantomime is still the predominant feature of the theatrical winter season in Great Britain.

Nowhere else in the world does King Pantomime reign so securely in the affections of the people. Every decent-sized town in the Kingdom has its own special pantomime which may run from a month to six or eight weeks continuously. The leading London comedians and comediennes look to the pantomine season for engagements at larger fees than they can earn during the rest of the year. Indeed I have known specially buxom young women who had difficulty in getting work at any other time being in special demand as "principal boys" while others, particularly qualified to play such parts as *Cinderella, Red Riding Hood, or Goody Two Shoes* were always sure of a long Christmas engagement even if they were unheard of for the rest of the year.

In the case of known performers a successful "panto" contract was, and still is, a passport for subsequent engagements at enhanced salaries. I have known artistes jump from five pounds a week to fifty merely as the result of hitting the high spots in some local pantomime. A pantomime audience is the most appreciative crowd of human beings that can be packed into any theatre. Everybody comes to enjoy themselves and if the fare provided is at all excellent the artistes have a "cinch" of a time.

I knew all this. Especially about the money to be made in panto! So when I was approached to sign an engagement to appear in "Aladdin" at the Theatre Royal, Glasgow, under the management of Messrs. Howard and Wyndham, the only

132

question I asked was "How much per?" To be quite honest I did not get what I asked for but as I had made a very liberal allowance for "argument" I was more than satisfied with the salary fixed up. If I say that it was in the region of two hundred pounds per week I will not be very far wrong. This was an extraordinary jump from the seven or eight pounds a "turn" I was earning in London—and would have had to go back to, if the pantomime proved a failure! So you may depend upon it I determined to leave nothing undone on my part to make "Aladdin" a triumphant success.

Which it was! I think it ran for thirteen weeks and we played to packed houses. All Glasgow went mad about this pantomime; even the railway companies ran special trains from the districts so that the people could see Harry Lauder as *Roderick McSwankey.* The "book" was as good a panto-mime story as has ever been put on the stage and Howard and Wyndham had got together a perfect combination of artistes for its presentation. There was Bessie Featherstone, one of the loveliest girls in the profession, as *Aladdin,* Dan Crowley as the Widow Twankey, Imro Fox as the Wicked Magician, Alice Russon as the Princess, and Jose Collins as the second girl. Poor Bessie Featherstone died in the middle of the run; Dan Crowley passed away several years later and Imro Fox is also dead. Alice Russon is, I believe, still alive and Jose Collins is today well-known as a musical comedy star both in this country and in America. Jose was only about sixteen years old and this Glasgow engagement was her first on leaving her convent school. She was an exceptionally pretty and vivacious girl but showed no promise at that time of becoming the beautiful singer she turned out to be in after years.

I had kept a "rod in pickle" for this pantomime in Glas-gow. From the day I signed the contract some months pre-viously I had been anxiously looking round for, and think-ing over, ideas for a new song or two. I wanted something really special. Not a burlesque, or a comic song, nor yet a character study; by this time I had quite a large repertoire of good songs, all of them popular and I knew that I could "get over" in pantomime with the material I had on hand. What I wanted was a jingling, simple love-lyric. I felt all the time that I would like to strike a new and dominant note. Then one night, on leaving a London theatre, the stage-door keeper handed me a letter. It was in a pink envelope, it had a seal on the back and the handwriting was in large sprawling letters.

"That's sure from a lady, Mr. Lauder," said the attendant. "I suppose you love a lassie?"

"Yes," I replied, "I do love a lassie—and I'm gaun awa' home to her noo."

I love a lassie! I love a lassie! I love a lassie! The words rang in my head all the way down to Tooting. I hummed them. I sang them to a dozen different musical phrases. I tried to get a verse out of them but the elusive something just failed me. A few nights later I met Mr. Gerald Grafton, a well-known London song-writer. I mentioned the phrase which had so impressed me. He was interested and said he would see what he could do with the idea. He worked on it and I worked on it, and at last we hammered out the framework of the song which I have sung in every part of the world during the past twenty-one years. It took Grafton and myself several weeks to get the words "just pat" but the melody I wedded to them came to me all at once and I do not think I ever afterwards altered a note of it. I knew I had got a great song. I knew it would be a winner. But I was scarcely prepared for the triumph it proved the first time I sang it on the opening night of the Glasgow Pantomime of 1905. The vast audience took the song to its heart instantly. Every night for thirteen weeks "I Love a Lassie" held up the action of the pantomime so long that it is a wonder to me the other artistes didn't enter a protest against my singing the song at all!

Had I only sung this song and done nothing else in the pantomime I think I would have been worth my salary to Howard and Wyndham. But I had a very "fat" part in the show—thanks to the man who wrote the book and to the extra work I was able to throw into my character of Roderick McSwankey. Roderick was supposed to be a young Glasgow boy who had apprenticed himself—for a premium of five shillings—to the Wicked Magician, who on his part, had agreed to teach Roderick all the tracks and alchemies of the Black Art. My constant anxiety, after parting with my five shillings, to keep in the closest personal touch with the Magician, never letting him out of my sight for a moment, proved to be much to the liking of the Glasgow people. Even in these early days, it seemed, I had earned a reputation for —shall we say?—financial shrewdness, and my repeated wailings about my "five shillin's" never failed to send the house into roars of merriment. I had some very good scenes, too, with a stage polar bear and there was a rich bit of comedy fooling between Dan Crawley and myself, both of us dressed up as women and talking scandal over a cup of tea and a cookie. Every now and then I poured a "wee drappie" from a half-mutchkin bottle into Dan's tea and the way he and I acted the garrulous women gradually getting "fou" was one of the hits of the show.

I sang several songs in this pantomime. One I recall was a female character song called "Once I had a Bonnie Wee Lad" and another was a song I had tried out in London and elsewhere entitled "Rob Roy McIntosh." They both went well but my great success was "I Love a Lassie." I think I sang this song for about three years without a stop. I couldn't get off the stage anywhere without singing it. Do I ever get tired of it, I am sometimes asked. Of course I do. I got so tired of singing "Lassie," as we call it in the family, that I determined to get a companion song to it. But this didn't materialize for several years until I struck "Roamin' In The Gloamin' " which is a story all on its own to be told later.

My work in that Glasgow Pantomime really put me on the map as a popular favourite in Britain. I was besieged with requests for "dates" all over the country but to each and every enquirer I had, alas, to give the same answer— sorry, am booked up for years ahead! My gramaphone records began to sell like hot cakes and here again I had reason to regret the precipitancy with which I had made arrangements during my early visits to London. It was no unusual thing for me to go to the recording offices and make half-a-dozen records in a day for a pound a time! Yes, "Tobermory," "Calligan," "She's Ma Daisy," "Stop yer Ticklin', Jock"—they all went for a "quid a nob"—or six songs for a fiver down!

It looked a lot of money to me in those days. Why, five pounds for singing a few songs was as much as a miner could earn by hard work in a fortnight! The Gramaphone Company of Great Britain did one of their best strokes of work when they got me "on the cheap." In justice to them, however, I must say that when my contracts with them came to be renewed they took a very generous view of my earlier stupidity and I have been very good friends with them and the Victor people of America for twenty years. A few years ago I signed a life-contract with the British company. Occasionally, when in a reflective mood or when going over the bank-book, I fall to dreaming of just how much money I ought to have earned from the millions and millions of gramaphone records of mine sold all over the two hemispheres. But it is always a painful business! Once I discussed the matter with my old friend Caruso and the figures he gave me from his angle made me so ill that I suddenly

"BUBBLES," A CHARACTER PART IN AN EARLY PANTOMIME

changed the conversation from "royalties" to voice production!

As so often happens in the most important happenings of a man's life I have never been exactly clear about the course of events which led up to my first visit to the United States. I know that previous to the Glasgow Pantomime one or two different people in the profession suggested that I should try a trip to America. But I did not pay the slightest heed to them. Some day, I told myself, I might be able to afford to cross the Atlantic for a holiday but the thought of playing to the American people certainly did not enter my head. Besides I was too keen on establishing my position in my own country. I must confess, however, that after my success in the pantomime at Glasgow—and at subsequent similar productions in Newcastle and Liverpool—it was rather galling to have to return to London and resume "turn" work under old contracts at something like a twentieth part of the money I had been earning in pantomine. I felt that I was every whit as good a draw in the music-halls as I had proved in the big Christmas productions. Indeed my return to the London stage after closing down in Glasgow saw me receive a series of the most extraordinary welcomes at the Tivoli and elsewhere ever given to a popular "star" in England. Crowded houses, tremendous enthusiasm and reams of newspaper publicity!

My London managers were, of course, delighted. But not one of them thought of coming to me and saying, "Lauder, old man, you're the biggest gold mine we have struck for years and I, for one, don't think it fair that you should only be getting seven or eight pounds a turn. I propose to scrap your existing contract and pay you a hundred!"

Oh, no, a contract was a contract! My pulling powers as an artiste were admitted but the managers did not forget to point out that they, on their side, had made bad contracts

with other artistes which they were compelled to stick to.
So that my success was really only balancing the losses they
were sustaining elsewhere. With this logical attitude I could
not, of course, quarrel and so I had just to grin and bear my
troubles as best as I could. But I made up my mind that
when the time came I would be amply revenged for what I
considered—wrongly, I grant you from a purely legal point
of view—was little short of a "grave miscarriage of justice."
Sure enough in after years I found myself in the position of
being implored by a well-known London manager to accept
a contract from him for two of his biggest halls.

"Tell him," I said to George Foster, then my agent, "that
he can have me for four hundred pounds a week!"

Foster rang me up in a few minutes and said he had
delivered my message, but that the poor man had had an
attack of heart disease on learning my terms. He was froth-
ing at the mouth and quite inarticulate. Could I not come
down in my price to a reasonable sum?

"Yes," said I, "I'll come down to four hundred and fifty!
And if he doesn't accept that my next "reduction" will be five
hundred. Ask him if he remembers refusing me an extra
pound twenty years ago!" The contract at four hundred
came along inside an hour.

There was one British manager, however, who always
gave me more than a straight deal. This was dear old Dennis
Clarke of Birkenhead. In the days when I was very young
he gave me one or two engagements every year. I think my
first salary with him was four pounds. At the end of the
week he gave me five. When my salary was seven he gave
me ten. And every year since then I have given Dennis a
date or two without there being so much as a "scrape o'
the pen" between us. He pays me what he thinks I have been
worth to him and I take it without even counting the money.
Again I can see some readers of these memoirs smiling a

sardonic smile over this last sentence. But it's the truth I'm
telling you. By his kindly treatment of me when I was a
struggling young chap in the latter years of last century
Dennis Clarke made a friend of me for life. He is a true-blue
Englishman. Poor old Dennis had had a rough time in health
of late, having lost a leg as the result of an accident. But his
great heart keeps him cheery. Here's tae ye, Dennis, me
lad! You've the "heart o' corn"—an' no mistake!

But I must get back to the story of how I ultimately fixed
up to go to America. It was all due, in the first instance, to
a lady! Her name escapes me for the time being—I may remember it afterwards—but she was the British representative of Messrs. Klaw and Erlanger, at that time one of the
largest firms of agents and impressarios in the United States.
She had heard me in London and in the provinces and had
written urging her principals in New York that I was a
most likely bird for an American "try-out," to put the
position no higher! The upshot was that they got in touch
with George Foster and he, in his turn, came to me at Manchester and reported that he had got a tentative offer for my
services for a five weeks run in New York—what did I say
about the scheme? I told Foster flat that I wasn't at all
interested in America. And in order to stop all further
negotiations I said I would only consider a trip if they
agreed to pay me—well, I mentioned a sum which I thought
would effectually put the brake on even American vaudeville
enterprise.

George set the cable working overtime at once and in a
day or two I was face to face with a contract which literally
made my mouth water! I forget just what I was earning
that week in Liverpool but it would not be more than £20.
The first thing to do was to ask Nance what she thought.
So I sent her a telegram to London telling her all about the
offer and asking her if she would go with me to America

in the event of the deal going through. Next morning I got
the following telegram from my wife.

Book of Ruth, Chapter One, Verse Sixteen.
Love Nance.

At first I couldn't understand what it was all about and
George Foster, who is a Jew and ought to have known all
about his biblical ancestors, was completely befogged. But
my old Sunday School training came to my rescue. I remembered vaguely the story of Ruth and Naomi—"Whither
thou goest I will go"—and on looking up the passage to get
the hang of it clearly I had certainly to hand it to Nance for
a most apt and affecting reply to my telegram. So, after
some more careful consideration, I signed my name on the
dotted line. At that time I thought it a great risk and I
remember that I sighed heavily.

CHAPTER TWELVE

"GREAT ARTISTE CAPTIVATES AMERICA"

I SET sail from Liverpool on the old *Lucania* in the middle of October 1907. Nance did not feel any too good in health at that time and cried off the trip. Tom, my inseparable henchman and companion, was ill with rheumatic fever in London and could not accompany me. So I took my son John, then a boy of sixteen and due to go up to Cambridge in a month or two. He had been over the water to Canada with his mother a year before; he was by way of being an old sailor and knew the ropes.

Poor John! I can scarcely bear to think about that trip with him and the fine times we had together on board. He was very young but he was very wise and among his other accomplishments he could play the piano beautifully and sing a good sentimental song. What a favourite he was with the passengers! Little did he or I dream then of a world war which was to bring desolation and unending sorrow into our home and into millions of others. How glad I am now that I took him with me on that first American trip! It was the longest time we had ever been together; we only got to know each other properly during that two months' holiday. Remembering always my first trip across the Atlantic with my dear boy John I never miss a chance of telling parents who are blessed with boys and girls to spend all the time they can with them when the bairns are young because if they don't do so then, they will be missing one of the purest joys of life in what Burns describes as "this melancholy vale."

As the ship drew nearer and nearer to New York I became quite nervous. I was about to launch another Scots "invasion." I knew well enough that America was the happy hunting-ground of thousands of my countrymen who had gone there before me; I was perfectly well aware of the fact that it was a magnificent land blessed by nature with a bountiful array of natural resources and inhabited by teeming and prosperous peoples drawn from every corner of the globe. I was fairly well acquainted with its history. George Washington and Abraham Lincoln ranked second only in my estimation to Robert Burns and Walter Scott; one of the greatest and grandest books I had read in my life up till then was "From Log Cabin to White House." Would there be a spotlight somewhere in this wonderful country for little Harry Lauder? What chance had I of competing with the cleverest entertainers in the vaudeville firmament of the mighty U. S. A.? Could I deliver the goods? Honestly, I felt dubious. I mentioned my doubts and fears to John, sitting with me in our stateroom two nights out from Sandy Hook. In language, and with an outlook far beyond his years, he replied:

"Dad, you'll be a riot! Don't you worry! I know America and the Americans (he had been in Canada for six weeks the previous year!) and they'll eat you up, bones an' all! But if you don't go down very well there are always plenty of ships home. My opinion is that you were right to come over here because if you can get away with it (he had all the little professional touches, you see) there's a bit of money to be cleaned up in the States. We'll do our best, anyhow!"

This "considered opinion" of John's cheered me up greatly. But next day I happened on something which sent my spirits slap down to zero. This was an old New York paper which I casually lifted up in the saloon and in glancing through which I came across a criticism of myself and my work written by a man signing himself Alan Dale. It was not only unkind; it was vitriolic. It not only criticised my art but it villified my personal appearance. It vomited scorn

on my songs, my singing of them, on my legs and the way
I walked with them, my nose and how I breathed through it;
it slashed, stabbed, and excoriated the British people for
laughing at me and wound up by asserting that the free
and discerning people of America would have none of "this
Scots buffoon who had the insolence to call himself a
comedian"—or words to that effect.

Grinding my teeth with rage I went in search of John.
You will remember that earlier in my memoirs I made the
statement that I have seldom or ever read a newspaper criticism of my stage work. This is absolutely true. I have never
been on the books of a Press Cutting Agency. Had I, like
so many celebrities, been in the habit of reading everything
said or written about me over a period of years, this snappy
column by Mr. Dale might have amused me immensely. As
it was it came to me like a blow on the jaw—and I saw red.
Moreover I was in a highly nervous condition on the very eve
of my inaugural performance in New York. I don't think I
ever saw a boy laugh so much as John did when he read the
Alan Dale criticism.

"Pa, this is splendid," said John. "It's the funniest thing
I've read in my life!" And he started to laugh all over again.

"I'm glad you think it funny, son," I growled. "It doesn't
sound at all funny to me. And if I meet this bloke Alan Dale
I'll plaster him up against the wa' like an *Answers* poster." I
meant it, too.

I was still smarting under the sting and injustice of Mr.
Dale's venom when we arrived at New York. As usual an
army of newspaper men came aboard and they all wanted
to interview me at once. Somehow or other I got it into my
head that one of the bunch must be the Dale bird! So I
refused to be interviewed until he stepped forward and confessed. "And I give him fair warning that I'll kill him on
the spot!" I added. The press boys all laughed, assuring me
that they had never heard of such an individual; in any case,

he wasn't one of the regular gang and I need not worry my head about him. But I was in no humour to be chatty that afternoon on the *Lucania* and I am afraid I made a very bad impression on the first crowd of New York pressmen to come in contact with Harry Lauder. One of the boys, in fact, pointedly told me that I was "a sour little guy," that I should "ease up on this fightin' stuff an' come across with a story or two," otherwise I would be "handed the frozen mitt in lil' ole New York!"

Klaw and Erlanger had sent down one or two representatives to the boat to meet me. But I think that in view of my stormy passages with the reporters they kept in the background. I heard afterwards that one of them went straight back to the office and gave a most disheartening account of my appearance and conduct. "Boss," he is reported to have said, "this guy Lauder has arrived all right. But he looks to me to be more a tragedy than a comedy. He's roarin' at the pier porters an' generally playin' hell with the noospaper men. Threatens to kill every critic in the States that don't stand for his act an' boost Scotland as the king nation of the universe! He's four foot nothin' in height, so short-sighted that he has to wear telescopes for eye-glasses, an' looks all of a cheap emigrant. Boss, you should see his old coat an' baggy trousers; I'll tell the world he ain't no snappy dresser. If this poor boob is a barnstormer, I'll throw in on an ace-full!" Naturally this news rather disconcerted the staff at Klaw and Erlanger's and I have no doubt the principals were already regretting their bargain. All the same they gave me a most kindly reception when we actually met next day.

If I had proved anything but a gold-mine to the reporters on the ship they got plenty of copy about me and my arrival in other directions. A very old British friend in Peter Dewar—then resident in New York and doing bright business in the sale of a Scots product now, alas, absolutely unknown in the States!—had arranged for several pipers in full Highland dress to "blaw me ashore" and lead the way from the pier to a tartan-draped motor-car in which I drove to the Knickerbocker Hotel.

Hundreds of expatriated Scots had also turned up at the harbour; they gave tongue to vociferous cries, Hielan' hoochs and shouts of welcome. This was all a surprise to me indeed. I had not expected anything like it. My intention had been all along to land in America very quietly, do my best to make a hit and, if I failed, to get away home again at once and regard my trip as an experience. We arrived on the Friday. On the Sunday I was so homesick that if there had been a steamer leaving New York that day I honestly think I would have booked a passage. But when Monday came I was on my toes—I had the I'll-show-'em feeling all right. John and I were at the New York Theatre, Times Square, an hour before I was due to go on at the matinée. The people rolled up all serene. When the programme opened the house was full. My number going up was the signal for a tremendous outburst of cheering, led, I have no doubt whatever, by my good Scottish friends and admirers.

Once again it was old "Tobermory" that did the trick. I had not been on the stage more than a minute before I realized that I was going to make good. At the end of my first song the applause was terrific. I forgot all about Old Man Dale, my doubts and forebodings of failure, and played as well as I have ever done in my professional career. "If this is New York I am going to love you," said I to myself. That was twenty years ago. I have never had the slightest reason to revise my decision.

At my first matinée I sang six songs in place of the three I had anticipated. But in the evening my reception was so warm that I had to sing ten numbers before I was allowed to leave the stage. Altogether I was "on" for just

over two hours, a physical ordeal which had me completely groggy at the finish. But I was happy in the knowledge that I had won out and that the gloomy prophecies
of my friend Mr. Dale had been falsified. Long before I
woke the next morning John went out and secured copies
of the leading New York dailies. He roused me up and
insisted on reading the very flattering and flowery comments of the theatrical and vaudeville critics on my performance and my triumph. There seemed to me to be as
many inches of headings as there was text to the laudatory
criticisms and one streamer cross-line remains in my mind.
It read—Harry Lauder, great artiste, captivates America.
As he laid down the last of the papers John turned to me
and said,

"Pa, dear, I knew you would paralyze them!"

I kissed John, turned over in my bed and went to
sleep again.

These first five weeks in America seem like a dream
to me now. Actually I *was* in dreamland most of the time.
Everything was so new and strange and vast and breathless that senses were in a "dwam" most of the time. I
must have met hundreds and hundreds of people whose
names I forget now but they were all very kind to me.
I had invitations to lunch, dinner, supper, and even breakfast. Prominent New Yorkers asked me to receptions,
dances, and functions of all kinds. I was completely rushed
off my feet. I began to think that life in New York was
a bit too strenuous for me and to weary for the peace and
quiet of working four halls a night in London! Whenever
I did manage to get an hour or two to myself I spent the
time wandering through the streets of New York, taking
stock of the immense buildings, watching the people hurry-
ing and scurrying hither and yon, taking trips on the sub-
way and in the street cars and generally trying to grasp
what New York stood for in the life of the new and won-

VIEWING NEW YORK FROM THE HOTEL KNICKERBOCKER ON THE OCCASION OF HIS FIRST
VISIT, IN 1907

derful world that had been opened up for me as if by magic. Here let me make a confession. After a week or two in the turmoil and frenzy I made up my mind that I liked the folks very much indeed but that I would sooner die than spend the rest of my days in New York! It "deaved" me to death. A sense of oppression came over me. I felt that of a certainty one or other of the big buildings would fall on me. The cumulative effect of all this was a sense of choking—I was always fighting for breath, as it were.

Two friendships I made on this visit which meant much to me then, and they have become stronger and stronger with the passage of time. Colonel Walter Scott swam into my ken the first week I opened at the New York Theatre. His breezy, straightforward, generous personality, added to the fact that he seemed to be more Scottish than I was myself, appealed to me at once. We fell for each other right away and have been "sworn brithers" for twenty years. An amazing man is Wattie Scott. A native-born American, and proud of it, he is yet the most perfervid lover of Scotland and all things Scottish that the world has ever seen. His affection for the land of his forebears is a religion with him. He is qualified to take a post as a professor of Scottish history and character in any university. The lore of Scotland from time immemorial is an open book to him; he sleeps with a copy of Burns beneath his pillow.

Walter is the perpetual president of a thousand St. Andrews' Societies and Burns' Clubs scattered throughout every state in the union; no Scottish Clan association is "worth a docken" if Wattie's name is not on its list of officebearers and financial supporters. All America knows what the colonel did in raising Scottish-American troops for the front in the time of the world war. Not content with his purely Scottish activities he is in the foreground of all good and charitable works in the United States; if there can be found anywhere in America half a dozen men or women willing to found a patriotic society to commemorate the Revolution, to perpetuate the name and fame of some illustrious poet, or writer or citizen or soldier or sailor or humanitarian or benefactory generally Wattie has only to be approached and all things are made smooth. If a bill has to be footed, he'll pay. If a speech is to be delivered he'll either do it himself or get the President to do it. If a thousand mile journey has to be undertaken in connection with any of his organizations he'll do it overnight and get back to his business in Broadway by the first available train. Where and how he finds time for one tenth part of the work he does has always been one of the monumental puzzles of America to me.

One of his latest ideas was to establish a great Scottish University on the Island of Iona in the Western Highlands. If it wasn't his he was at least all over it. Walter asked me if I would subscribe to this great and glorious notion. "Certainly not!" I told him, "I've seen Iona and a university there would have as much chance as an ice factory leaning up against the North Pole!" But that's the sort of man he is. Just a great big, open-hearted boy anxious and willing to take the whole wide world into his arms and organize it on Clan Association lines. He'll never know how much I love and respect him.

Another personal friendship I cemented during this first visit was between myself and William Morris. No need to tell you that Will Morris is today the greatest vaudeville agent on both sides of the Atlantic. In those days he was Klaw and Erlanger's chief booking man and I had a lot to do with him while at the Times Square Theatre. Between this black-haired, handsome Jew with the little nose and the "gripping" wee Scots comedian with the big nose a mutual affection sprang up. We took to each other from the very

outset. I always say that Will Morris is the best Jew I have
ever met and he says I am the best Scotsman he has ever
met—so what more is there to be said? Nothing! Later he
became my American manager. Under his wing I have made
twenty trips to America and he has "put me across" in
practically every town and city of any size in the States
from New York to San Francisco and from Mexico to the
Canadian border. And I have never had a written contract
with Morris from the first day in Liverpool, in the year
1908, when we settled our original bargain with a shake of
the hand. For all his success and world-wide popularity with
all manner of theatrical people Will is a shy man and I
should hate to make him blush by saying just what I think
of him. Since meeting him and hooking up together I have
got to know exactly what is meant by "the chosen people."
All the same, mind you, I think Morris must have made a
lot of money out of me. But, as I haven't done so badly
myself as the result of our association, I am content to let
it go at that! (Don't you think, Will, that I should have
just a wee bit more out of my next annual farewell tour in
view of the fine character I have given you in this book?)

When my engagement came to a close at the end of the
five weeks Klaw and Erlanger were most anxious that I
should either stay on in America or sign another contract
to appear under their management at the very earliest date
on which I could get released from my British bookings.
As I had had a devil of a job to get away from these bookings for two months I did not see how I could remain a day
longer. As for a new contract, well, I wanted time to consider everything in its due proportion. I was evidently a big
hit in America—a wow! That was a fact which admitted of
no shadow of doubt. Before the end of my first week I had
been stormed at with requests to appear in every large city
in the States. Several of the big Scottish societies had even
offered me as much for one night's appearance as I had been

drawing in salary at the New York Theatre. In short, I could see that there was a rich and fallow field for me in the New World. But I determined to gang warily in the matter of putting my signature to legal documents. I had had bitter experience of hasty decisions in this respect at home.

"Harry, ma lad," said I to masel', "there's nae hurry. America's waitin' for ye an' wants ye. America is ready tae weigh in wi' the dollars good an' plenty. Ye've sown the good seed—awa' hame an' wait for it tae bear fruit abundantly."

Realizing that this was sound common-sense I refused all temptations to get me to stay on. But lest my resolution should fail me at the last moment I packed up the night before John and I should have sailed and went down to the *Carmania* and locked myself in the cabin. Two o'clock the next afternoon would have been time enough. Urgent messages, letters, and telegrams continued to arrive at the hotel many hours after the ship had sailed. And that, very briefly is the story of how I broke into America.

It was only a flying visit, undertaken with no great enthusiasm, and it never took me out of the confines of New York. But it was the precursor of many wonderful and delightful tours which have made me better acquainted with the people of the United States than perhaps any other traveller in the world. Indeed I must have seen, and been seen by, more citizens of the Republic than any other man who ever lived! This seems at first blush a pretty tall statement. But work it out for yourself and you will see that I am not far wrong. Tom and I once sat down during a long railroad journey from North to South and tried to calculate how many miles we had travelled in the States together. We lost count completely after we had got to our first hundred thousand.

CHAPTER THIRTEEN

'ARRY LAUDAH'S 'OSS

THE two weeks that I spent on the Atlantic going and coming from America on the occasion of that memorable first visit were the longest, and incomparably the most delightful holidays I had ever had in my life up till then. Unforgettable, too, on account of the companionship and comradeship of John, all of whose rosy prognostications of my success—"bones an' all"—had been so completely fulfilled. I came to love Dr. Atlantic, the greatest medical man in the world. Honestly I do not think I could ever have achieved my record of world-work—four times round the globe and twenty visits to America, singing every day and often twice a day, Sundays and travelling days excepted—had it not been for the months I have spent on shipboard with the winds of heaven blowing away all the cobwebs and filling the lungs and the blood with new energy and fire. The busy business men and industrial leaders of America know all about Dr. Atlantic. They appreciate him much more than our people do. A week under his ministrations—sometimes, let me admit, very drastic ministrations—and you step off his floating consulting-room feeling fit to knock a house over. That was how I felt on the *Carmania* coming home that first trip. The only thing I didn't like was the sense of idleness and not earning anything so I paced up and down the deck trying to get a new song to the beat of my feet on the pitch-pine. I got it right enough. "When I Get Back Again to Bonnie Scotland" was thought out and more or less welded together on the promenade deck of the old *Carmania*. I never wrote a better marching air than the lilt to which the words of this song are set. It was an instantaneous hit when

151

I put it on in London a week or two later. I am told it was a favourite song with the Scottish troops in France. And I sang it hundreds of times many years after in camps, ruined chateaux, and other places behind the line on my visits to France under the auspices of the British Government during the war.

With the exception of my pantomime engagements my trip to New York had earned me more money than I had ever before secured and I was a very proud man when I reckoned up that I was now worth perhaps a couple of thousand pounds in addition to my house at Tooting which had been purchased, or at least finally paid for, out of my pantomime earnings. My great idea about this time was to be independent. I remember telling myself over and over again that any man who had a house of his own and five thousand pounds in the bank should be able to hold up his head with the best and look the whole world fearlessly in the face. This hankering after independence is inborn in most Scots, especially in those who, like myself, have been reared in poverty and who have bitter memories of fathers and mothers striving and struggling and fretting themselves into their graves in order to make ends meet and give their dear bairns some reasonable chance in the battle of life. I decided that I would never rest until I had saved enough money to keep me and mine if the day should arrive when I lost my voice or my popularity. I had seen so many "stars" in an improvident and always uncertain profession come to financial grief that my resolve was strong to save all that I could and so hasten the day of independence for myself and my loved ones. There were to be no "charity benefits" for Harry Lauder!

But the small salaries I had to come back to in London —these old contracts again!—did not allow me much scope for "makin' mickle mair" as Burns has it. I was now the undisputed "top-liner" of the British vaudeville stage. I

"WHEN I WAS TWENTY-ONE"

never played to anything but a crowded house. Often there
were artistes on the same bill with me getting twice, three
times, yes, ten times my salary but I was always the drawing card. The public loved me and I loved playing to them.
The managers loved to have me—so much so that when I
wanted a few days off to nurse a cold or merely to take
a rest they insisted on having a doctor's certificate. They
didn't believe me! But latterly I found a way of circumvent-
ing the official doctors sent down to Tooting to find out if
Lauder was malingering. I would jump into bed just before
the medico arrived and it was an easy thing for me to
assume a drawn and doleful expression and to work up a
cough which would have convinced the whole College of
Surgeons that I was in a state of incipient consumption. It
always worked. Indeed one doctor went back to London and
reported that poor Harry Lauder was not long for this
world. This "stage" cough which I developed so skilfully
about this time came in very handy many years later when
I sang my song "When I was Twenty-One." Every time I
sing the song and start the old man's cough in the patter
I feel that I want to laugh, remembering how I fooled the
managers' doctors many years ago. But please do not think
that I made a practice of getting out of a "cheap engagement." Certainly not; I played every contract I ever made,
either on the date arranged or subsequently, and for the
money agreed upon. But it *was* very galling to me in these
early days to feel that certain people were determined,
Shylock-like, to get their exact pound of flesh from me no
matter whether I was feeling well or ill. And I only tell
you the story to show how sure a money-spinner I was in
the eyes of the managers.

However, what I was losing on the swings, I was making
on the roundabouts. In the early years of this century it was
a very common thing for the rich and titled people of the
West-end of London to give great private entertainments at

their town mansions. For these I was in much demand. I could have accepted private engagements almost every night of the week at very handsome fees. But I only went out for the "big stuff" and to the élite of the West-end mansions. At the Tivoli I was perhaps drawing eight or ten pounds a week yet it was no uncommon thing for me to refuse ten times that amount for half-an-hour's singing in some great lady's salon after midnight. The favourite song at these functions was always "I Love a Lassie"; indeed I had to make a definite bargain with more than one hostess that this song would be included in my list. There can be few of the really great London mansions that I have not sung in at one time or another. At these private entertainments the guests liked to join in the choruses and I have had Royal Princes and Princesses, Dukes and Duchesses, Earls and Countesses, Lords and Ladies all shouting my choruses at the pitch of their voices.

I think I must always have been a lucky man in the way of free advertisement. Already I have told you how I did nothing to stop, but rather to foster, the rumours and stories about certain supposed Scottish characteristics which had become, so to say, over-developed in my personality. But this was by no means the only publicity I got. Everything I did for months after my return from America seemed to find its way into the papers. If I got a present of a bull-dog from an old Scottish admirer its photograph appeared in twenty different papers. If I bought an American motor-car for John there was a "story" about it and John was photographed driving it, standing beside it, or underneath it. If he ran it into a neighbour's wall—as he did—the neighbour was interviewed and there were photographs of the "gash." If I put on my kilt and went down to Brighton of a Sunday for a whiff of the sea the news was in the London papers next morning. I couldn't move a leg in bed, or go to a barber's for a hair-cut, or buy a second-hand overcoat—as

I certainly once did in a theatrical costumer's shop in London—but it duly appeared in print. If any of my audiences were more than usually demonstrative there was a paragraph headed "Lauder's Triumphant Return" or "Harry's Amazing Reception." Even the sober and responsible writers like Archer, and James Douglas and Edgar Wallace, John D. Irvine and many others all took to writing analyses of my art and stage achievements. For me it was quite bewildering. Had I had a "soft patch" in my make-up all this praise and notoriety would sure have found me out to my undoing. "Of course you had a very clever press-agent" some of you will say. The only press-agent I ever had in my life was entirely unpaid. I refer to my life-long friend and pal Willie Blackwood, now a very well-known journalist and one of the directors of the Amalgamated Press, London, the largest periodical publishing house in the world. I forget just how many millions of papers and magazines this amazing British firm of publishers distributes every week but I think it is in the region of ten millions. The only other printing combination in the world to compare with it is in Philadelphia. "Wullie" certainly pulled lots of stunts about his chum Harry Lauder in the old days when he lived in Glasgow and he was almost as well-known in the London and provincial theatres as Tom and I were. But in his case it was a pure labour of love. Only the other night we were sitting in his house at Harrow recalling the old days over a pipe and a "wee deoch" and we both agreed that no performer in the world had got more publicity—and paid less for it—than me.

Willy-nilly, something was always turning up to focus my name in the minds of the public. Take the case of the horse which appeared with me on the stage of the London Pavilion when I put on a song entitled "The Man They Left Behind," a comic soldier study of a peculiarly ridiculous description. For the purpose of the song I required a horse, preferably a funny horse. But there are no serious or funny horses; there are just horses. That is, generally speaking. So I set out to get a horse which would at least give the song a background. Letting my desires be known to a Lambeth horse-dealer I was assured by return of post that he had "just the animal I would have selected out of ten thousand."

" 'Arry, ole top," said the dealer when I went down to his yard, "this 'orse I got 'as been waitin' for twenty years for you! God knows 'ow old he is but if you can get 'im on the stige he'll make the people ill larfin'. Just come an' be interjooced to 'im!"

We walked into the stable, a ramshackle building falling to pieces and presenting signs, both to eyes and nose, of not having been cleaned since it was built. In the furthest away stall stood the most ghastly-looking equine—a night-mare of a horse. He was leaning up against the stone wall of the stable, his head hanging down so far between his front legs that two long tufts of hair on his upper-lip were touching the cobbled floor. Almost every bone in his body could have been counted and his forelegs were bent outward so far that it was a wonder to me he was able thus to support even his frail weight in front. This caricature of a horse had only one good eye—good, that is, in so far as it was complete. An accident to the other had had the effect of leaving it permanently at half-cock. Immediately I went up to him he fixed his good eye on me, slowly slewing round and raising his head the better to do so. I swear Old Scraggy—as I instantly dubbed him—laughed at me. I most certainly laughed at him, laughed so loudly and so long that Tom had to help me from the stable.

"How long do you think he'll live?" I asked the dealer. "If you can guarantee him for a month I'll make him a national horse-character!"

"Lorlumme, 'Arry," said the dealer, "e's bin pullin' two ton o' coal every day for years and surely you ain't goin'

to work 'im harder than that! He'll live as long as you'll
sing your new song any'ow."

He was right—exactly right. Old Scraggy was sent up to
the Pavilion on the Monday night. Tom and I had thought
out some humorous "equipment" for him. He had cricket
pads on his fore feet, a frowsy "moo-poke" (food-bag) was
fastened on to his straggly tail and the saddle consisted
of an old piece of Axminster carpet kept in position by
"girths" of string and old rope. He wore blinkers that
flapped from side to side as he walked and generally he was
the most comical bit of live stage property imaginable.
There were shrieks of laughter in the wings as Tom and I
put the finishing touches on Old Scraggy's accoutrements
but they were nothing to the tornado of merriment which
greeted the two of us as we "galloped" on to the stage. At
the very first performance "Scraggy" showed some hesitancy
about facing the footlights and one of the stage hands
prodded him with the sharp end of a pencil. The result
was that he made one jump forward clear of the wings,
stopped dead, and sent me shooting over his head as if I
had been discharged from a catapult. Luckily I was not hurt
and scrambled to my feet amid terrific yells of laughter
from the audience who thought that the whole episode had
been carefully arranged. "Scraggy" stayed put in the position he assumed after his initial jump and never moved a
muscle for the rest of the performance. Or rather I should
say his body and legs were absolutely immovable but his
head sank lower and lower as the song went on. The audience
never stopped laughing at him all the time; indeed, "The
Man They Left Behind" was a very funny song but it
didn't have anything in this respect on my steed who was
easily the most humorous "silent performer" on the London
stage during his "run."

The papers were full of "Scraggy" stories, where I got
him, what I was paying for his services, what I fed him on.

One journal even had a column interview with the horse on "What I think of Harry Lauder—By Scraggy." So famous did this extraordinary quadruped become that crowds assembled every night at the Pavilion stage-door to see his arrival and departure. His journey to the theatre was a nightly West-end sensation and 'Arry Laudah's 'Oss became notorious. One evening he slipped up in Piccadilly Circus and as he was very tired after his walk from Lambeth he refused to rise. It required the united efforts of ten policemen and as many civilians to get him on his feet and he had literally to be carried to the sidepath, where he stood stock-still for fully a quarter·of an hour. After this breathing spell, and entirely of his own volition, his attendant having mysteriously disappeared in search of some liquid refreshment, he ambled off in the direction of the Pavilion accompanied by several policemen and a crowd of highly amused pedestrians. Scraggy was funnier than ever that night because he was covered with mud which we had no time to remove. Poor Old Scraggy! Two days after I finished my season at the Pavilion, and having opened a provincial tour at Edinburgh, I learned from the papers that the old horse had been found dead in his Lambeth bed. The excitements of a stage life had been too much for him. His success had killed him! But he provided me with a vast amount of free publicity and had I been in London I would have seen that old Scraggy's mortal remains were saved from the last indignity of the Cats' Meat Man's barrow!

Even when I was reading of Scraggy's death I was having another experience of a different kind with another stage horse. "The Man They Left Behind" had been so popular in London that I resolved to sing the song, equine partner and all complete, on my provincial tour. So at Edinburgh I had to get a horse for the part. Early on the Monday morning of my Edinburgh week I went down to the well-known horse emporium of the Messrs. Croall and told the folks there that I required an animal that would not be frightened at music and the strange surroundings of the footlights. I was told that they would send up one of the quietest horses in the stable and one that wouldn't be upset by all the military or bagpipe bands in Scotland. I was content to leave the matter in the hands of Croalls, being the more ready to do this in that I rather prided myself on my knowledge of horses and ability to manage them. You see I had been a pony-driver in the mines for some time and you get "gey thrawn wee deevils" among the underground horses. The horse sent up to the Empire on the Monday night was quiet enough in the wings and submitted to all the strange trappings we put on him without a symptom of annoyance. He even carried me on to the stage all right and began to look around with what I thought was an intelligent interest. But all of a sudden, as I was doing the "walk round" for my first chorus he laid his ears back and made to savage me as I passed the side of the stage nearest to him. I made a very real start away from him. Again the audience thought this was all in the play and they yelled their hearty approval. "Peter" as I called this Edinburgh horse, had his attention thus diverted from me and walked down to the very edge of the footlights and stared quizzically at the people in front. This was another bit of "acting" much to the liking of the audience and it certainly made a hit with me too at the moment. The number finished in fine style, I caught hold of "Peter," mounted him and rode off the stage. His exit was a trifle spirited, I must admit, for he "breenged" up against the scenery, clattered across the prompt side and very nearly came to grief among some "props" lying there for a later act. I narrowly escaped being precipitated down a stairway leading to the proscenium. All the same we had made a very fine start as a double-act and I was quite pleased with Peter's eccentricities which I put down to mere playfulness. Next night, however, he was in high fettle and had evidently made up his mind to do things. He started by prancing about the stage so much that I could not get on with the song. Sometimes I was running after him; more often he was running after me —and I didn't half like the look in his eye, either!

Suddenly he started to back in the direction of the orchestra. I seized hold of the reins and began to pull. The harder I pulled the more he backed. The people rocked in their chairs with merriment, thinking that this was some glorious new stunt with a comic horse that Harry Lauder had invented for their amusement. When, however, the drummer in the orchestra looked up and found a horse's tail swishing directly over his head he beat a hasty retreat from his place and his action was followed by several members of the band nearest to him. Two or three of the occupants of the first row of stalls likewise hurried away to safety. Soon the whole house was in an uproar. Those who were out of reach of all possible danger continued to scream with uncontrollable laughter but the remainder of the musicians and the people in the front seats started a general stampede. My wife was a terrified spectator from the wings and I could hear her shouting to the stage hands to go on and help me to "pull the brute back before he killed somebody!" Just when it seemed a certainty that the horse would make a very undignified descent on to the big drum it occurred to him to look round and see where he was going, so to speak. After a moment or two of hesitation he sprang forward. The tension on the reins thus suddenly broken, I went heels over head up-stage, my steed jumped over my body and went dashing into the wings, foaming at the mouth. The stage hands flew for their lives but "Peter's" attendant soon had him under control. That was his last night as my "assistant." Afterwards I had a horse of a much more docile disposition, greatly to the relief of the drummer and his musical associates.

CHAPTER FOURTEEN

WILL MORRIS COMES FOR ME

I HAVE always thoroughly enjoyed my provincial tours in England, Scotland, and Ireland. Wherever I go I get real good entertainment during the day fishing, golfing or shooting. After Edinburgh and Glasgow on the trip of which I am writing I played Southport, in Lancashire. One day I had gone out with a friend to have a round of golf forgetting that George Foster, my agent, and a London manager named Harry Masters, were coming up to see me on an important business matter. When they arrived and were informed that I had gone golfing they said they would like to see what sort of a game this golf business really was. Neither of them had ever played it or seen it. As a matter of fact golf had not then taken England by storm as it has since done. There were lots of courses but comparatively few players. So Foster and Masters did not think they were doing anything amiss when they marched on to Formby Golf Course in silk hats, frock coats, and white spats. By the time they walked out across the links and made up to us we were playing the fifth or sixth hole. I told them to walk behind with Tom and "watch how the game was played." But I don't think they paid much attention until Tom, always keen on a practical joke, noticed that the pocket-strap of my golf bag was unfastened and that a fine new ball—one of two I had bought at the professional's shop before setting out—had dropped on to the fairway. "Hullo," said Tom on coming up with the ball, "somebody has lost a ball here. Better pick it up, George. It's worth two bob and Harry is always willing to buy a good ball cheap—he'll maybe give you a shilling for it!"

161

Foster did as he was told, never suspecting that his leg (to say nothing about mine) was being pulled. "I've just found this new ball, 'Arry," he said. "Is it worth a shilling to you?" I took the ball, examined it, and decided that it was worth all of that amount. Foster took his shilling and fell back to join Masters and Tom. A few holes later Harry Masters came to me with another new ball, said he had found it on the course, and asked me what I would give him for it. "The same as George got!" I replied, forking out another shilling and congratulating both silk-hatted gentlemen on their ball-finding proclivities. "In fact," I added, "I think I'll stop playing and have a look round myself for balls; the Formby golfers seem to lose a lot!" At this stage Tom, as he told me afterwards, was on the point of explaining the "joke" when another ball trickled between Foster's legs. It had been driven by one of the plus-2 men of the club playing a game behind us. Foster instantly stooped down, picked up the ball and promptly offered it to me for another shilling. As I had not seen the ball coming, being too intent on my own game, I took it from him and was examining it with a view to purchase when loud yells from the rear caused us to look round. One of the Formby members was waving his driver in the air and saying words which sounded to me tolerably like an outburst of general cursing. As I pocketed the "found" ball and was dipping into my trouser-pocket for still another shilling to pass over to Foster the player behind came dashing up with wild oaths directed not to any one of us but to, as he phrased it, "the whole damned thieving bunch of you!"

Tom, the scoundrel, turned away choking with laughter. Foster, rather a dignified person at all times, turned upon the stranger with a speech beginning "How dare you——?" But he got no further for the Formby member—one of the most fluent and original specialists in swearing I have come across in a long life-time—denounced us singly, and as a company, for the most contemptible and villainous gang of thugs and outsiders that had ever had the nerve to spoil the landscape of a respectable golf course. Foster and Masters he described as a "couple of damned quack-doctors from the beach at Blackpool" while I was "worse than the caddies who stole balls from a player's bag because I was at least dressed like a golfer and ought to know better than buy balls picked up by my overdressed friends before they had stopped rolling!"

By this time I deemed it expedient to take a hand in the argument but the information, given in what was intended by me to be convincing and dramatic style, that "I was Harry Lauder and ought to explain that my friends from London did not ken much about golf"—rather added fuel to the fire of the Formby man's wrath and off he started again. He passed some particularly pungent and personal remarks about myself, hinted that he was more than disposed to credit all the stories he had heard about me in view of the first-hand knowledge he now had as to how I got my golf-balls, and vowed that the local police should be called in to deal with the whole disgraceful situation.

Had it not been for Tom I do not know what the end of it all would have been. He came forward, still laughing hilariously, and explained the joke he had played not only on Foster and Masters but on myself. Immediately I heard the staggering news that I had been buying my own golf-balls I hastily opened the pocket of my bag, assured myself that it was true, and rounded on Foster and Masters with a vocabulary second only in quality and selectness to that of the Formby member. Having now something to laugh at himself, the edge of his anger was turned and an hour later the episode was declared ended and all wounds were healed at the nineteenth hole.

One golf story leads to another and while I am at it I may as well tell you what happened to me at the Auckland

Course in New Zealand. The first time I played here some years ago I had the same caddie for two days running but on the third day a strange boy came up to the first tee and handed me my driver. "Hullo," said I, "you're not the same boy as I had yesterday and the day before—is he ill?"

"No, Sir Harry," said the lad, "he's quite well!"

"Then why is he not caddying for me today?" I asked.

"Well, sir, we tossed for it today—I mean we tossed which of us should carry for you," replied the boy, looking just a bit sheepish or sulky—I wasn't sure which. I must confess that I felt a little elated that the New Zealand caddies should toss among each other for the honour of carrying my clubs.

"So you won, did you?" I went on.

"No, sir," came back the prompt answer, "I lost!" Think it over, folks!

They tell a good story about me at an Australian course through which a railway runs. At one of the holes you have to drive over the rails. I had a very nice game with two or three "birdies" in the round and was feeling so good that I perhaps erred on the side of generosity in the way of a tip to my caddie at the finish. Immediately on returning to the "pen" he was asked by the other caddies what I had given him. "Five shillings," he proudly remarked and showed the two half-crowns. "Gee!" exclaimed one of his companions, "you must have saved his life at the railway crossing!"

Of the hundreds of golf courses all over the world on which I have played I think my own home course at Kirn, in Argyllshire, is the loveliest from a scenery point of view. The vistas of mountain, moor, and loch which you get from many of the tees there are unexcelled. Every time I play a round at Kirn it takes me about four hours because I simply have to stop after every other shot and lose myself for a few minutes in a spell-bound admiration of scenes of majestic loveliness. The golf, too, is quite hard enough for me. If I shoot anything round 90 I think I have played above myself. Of course there are no railway engines to help me at Kirn as there are at Monifieth in Forfarshire, that little golf-mad town which has sent so many professionals to earn fame and fortune in America. Once I was playing a game there with Willie Blackwood. The first hole runs alongside the railway track its entire distance. On this occasion I drove off, sliced my ball so badly that the driver of a slow goods train saw it coming, caught it in his hands and dropped it out on the first green. It was lying "dead" when I came up to it and I got a two at a pretty hard four hole! How's that for an untrue golf story?

But this one is really true. Only a few days ago I went over with Blackwood to his club at Oxhey, that beautiful course near London presided over—professionally—by the genial giant, Ted Ray. As we had booked a time by 'phone the news leaked out that I was going to perform and there was quite a group of members of both sexes round the tee when we arrived. Before leaving Harrow, however, we got hold of a very old and filthy golf-ball which Blackwood's dog had been playing with in his garden for perhaps a couple of months. Unless this ball was used in association with a club of some kind nobody would have been able to tell what it was. It wasn't even round. Arrived at the tee I solemnly took this monstrosity from my pocket, handed it to the caddie and ordered him to tee it up. The lad started to laugh but I was as solemn as a judge. "What the devil are you laughing at, boy?" I asked sternly. "The b-b-ball, sir," stammered the caddie. "What's wrong with the ball, boy?" I demanded. "I've played with it for four years. Put it down—a good high tee!" The caddie teed up and, wonderful to relate, I hit a beauty with it, the unshapely, dirty mass hurtling through the air for a good hundred and fifty yards. As "Wullie" and I moved off, not the semblance of a smile on our faces, we heard gasps, titters and "Well, I'm damned!'s" from the astonished Oxhey members and I know for a fact that it took "Jock" Anderson, the popular Scottish captain of Oxhey who was in the know of our prank, quite a long time to prevail on the horrified members that I really put down a clean ball after the first shot!

But to revert back to my stage work. As the months went on I began again to think about America and how nice it would be to get back there again and touch some real money. I had kept in correspondence with Will Morris since my return. Every letter I had from him contained a sentence or two about my great success there and a hint that I had only to say the word and he would fix me up for a much longer tour at a salary which would make my earnings at home look like chicken-feed. Then all at once, without even saying he was coming, Will walked into my dressing-room at Liverpool. We shook hands. Will said, "When shall we sail?" I said, "Just as soon as you can prevail on my British managers to release me—and that'll be never!" But Morris and George Foster between them managed the apparently impossible—at a price! I forget just how much "consolation money" we had to pay certain managers for their agreement to release me but I remember that the sum made my blood boil and it was only the thought that I would come out all right on balance that induced me to make the trip.

While saying this I must at the same time admit that the call of America was very strong. There is an electrical something in the air of the United States and the great Dominion of Canada which, once it inoculates one's blood, cannot easily be resisted. Perhaps it is the freshness, the vitality, the Spirit of Youth which animates the peoples of the New World. If it is not these things I cannot define the lure—quite apart, believe me, from monetary considerations—America has always had for me. I have been going

SIR HARRY AND WILL MORRIS ON THE DECK OF THE *AQUITANIA*
"Good-bye, Will, but I'll Soon be Back Again"

over there for more than twenty years now and although
my work is harder, much more strenuous, across the water,
I feel a new inspiration every time I land in New York or
Montreal for still another tour. Yes, as I write these lines
in Dunoon I find my mind wandering all over North America and I see rising before my eyes familiar forms and faces
that I have come to love very much. This "America Calling"
urge reminds me of the story about the Scottish minister
who had accepted, in ecclesiastical language, "a call from
God to another sphere of usefulness." His leading elder,
discussing the vacancy thus created in the local church, remarked to the senior deacon that "it was a funny thing that
God aye seemed to call his meenisters awa' to a bigger
steepend!"

My second trip lasted for fourteen weeks. On this
occasion I played ten weeks in New York and a week each
in Boston, Philadelphia, Pittsburgh, and Chicago. I thought
my previous experience of New York had taught me all
there was to know about the States and its people. What a
terrible mistake! One only gets to know the soul of a nation
when one begins to work outward from its great towns
and cities. So you will realize how interested I was in visiting the four wonderful cities I have mentioned. The week
I spent in each of them convinced me that my American
education was only beginning. Chicago is as different from
New York as London is from Edinburgh; Boston might
be on another continent so far as its comparison with Pitts-
burg is concerned! While Philadelphia is again completely
different from every other American city. It is more like a
British city than any other place in the United States and
that is probably the reason why many British visitors have
told me they feel perfectly at home there. I always do—but
then I have travelled America so thoroughly, and am a
"freeman" of so many of its chief cities, that I am and feel
quite at home in any place from coast to coast. It is not my

intention in these memoirs to embark on any sort of "appreciation" of the United States, its towns, their inhabitants and their characteristics. For one thing I could not do justice to such an important and fascinating subject and even if I attempted it I am no Will Rogers on such a lay and the result, while it would be flattering to my friends the American people, would be extremely disappointing judged as a literary effort. The only real thought behind this paragraph is my suggestion that it is always a dangerous thing hastily to judge a people or a country from a flying visit to one or two of the big centres. After my first trip to New York I was under the impression that America was an open book to me and that I, shrewd fellow, had not taken long to weigh up its people, their mannerisms, their characteristics, their amazingly numerous good points and—well, their weaknesses. This extended tour the following autumn only served to show me how little I knew and to embue me with the desire to become better and better acquainted with a country the vastness, the richness, the variety, the resources and possibilities of which made a tremendous impression on my mind. In later years and under exceedingly difficult circumstances the knowledge I acquired of America and the Americans during my earlier trips was to stand me in good stead when I became an unofficial ambassador of Britain—a Britain stricken, gasping, but defiantly determined to see a Big Thing through.

From a professional point of view my second vaudeville engagement in the States was even more successful than my first. The audiences took me and my songs to their hearts; I was as happy as a king—a lot happier than most kings I have met! And there was a smile on Will Morris's face that became broader and broader as the nightly "returns" were handed to him. Frequently I would "keek ower his shouther" to have a look at the figures for myself and what I saw made distinctly good reading, mind I'm tellin' ye.

Often I would nervously ask Will if he thought the Lauder vogue would last in the States.

"Last, Harry!" he would exclaim, "Why, we have only started to scratch the soiface; we ain't got down to the real gold-vein yet. We'll be diggers for ten years to come!" Saying which Will would show his white teeth and blink his eyes so rapidly that you couldn't tell the colour of them!

While the native Americans certainly rolled up in their thousands, encouraged to do so by the extraordinarily kind criticisms of my performances which constantly appeared in the newspapers, there is no doubt in my mind that the exiled Scots in the States had more to do with my success than many people imagined. We are easily the most "clannish" race in the world. We love each other even if we don't trust each other. Wherever we scatter ourselves over the Seven Seas we seem to smell each other out and gravitate as surely as Newton's law operates. Let one Scot be attacked in a wilderness or on a cannibal island and another will pop up from nowhere to his rescue. Put a Scot in the Mayor's chair of any city in the world and he'll have to spend more than half his time finding jobs for people from his own home town. Rustle a bag of money anywhere and the Scot will beat the Jew to it every time. The expatriated Caledonians sure rallied to my support during my earlier trips to Dollar Land. Not only so, they turned up at my shows in all manner of Scottish costumes—in kilts, with Balmoral bonnets, wearing tartan ties, and many of them brought their bagpipes with them. They imparted an enthusiastic atmosphere to my appearances everywhere; their weird shouts and "hoochs" and skirls provided good copy for the journalists and next-day talking points for the natives. In the first twenty weeks I spent in the States I must have met personally ten thousand people who claimed acquaintance with me in "the auld days in Hamilton, Harry!"—or Glasgow, or Arbroath, or Portobello, as the case might be. I shook hands with them all, lied fluently when I told them I recognized them, and presented signed post-cards to one at least out of every fifty!

Apropos of this rallying of the Scotties to my banner one of the most affecting incidents of my life occurred on the opening night of my second tour in New York. Before going on the stage I was handed a note signed by a Scot who said he had come all the way from Klondyke to hear me. He had a personal message from five hundred miners up there to deliver to me—would I give him a few minutes after my turn was over? Of course I told Tom to wait at the stage door and bring him round. In due course the man from Klondyke appeared, a big, burly, rough-and-ready chap hailing originally from Ayrshire. The tale he told me made the tears come to my eyes. There were many Scots in the mining camp he came from and when they heard that Harry Lauder was to appear in New York they decided to organize a sweepstake the winner of which would have all his expenses paid to New York and back again. The only conditions laid down were that the lucky winner should secure the full words of all my songs (and as much of the melodies as possible of the unpublished numbers) and bring back a signed photo of myself to prove that the delegate had had actual personal contact with me. My visitor had drawn the lucky number and had arrived in New York the previous Friday after being on the road fully a fortnight. He told me that in addition to the Scots who organized the sweepstake hundreds of other miners had taken tickets and it was not until all the tickets had been sold that the awful thought arose in the minds of the promoters—what if an American, or an Irishman, or a Pole or a German won the prize? "Fortunately my name came out of the bag first," said the Ayrshire man, "and here I am. Gosh, but I've had the time o' ma life, Mr. Lauder. And now I'll go back happy!" I got Tom to give him notes of all the songs and lyrics which

were not on sale and secure copies of those that were. I
also prevailed on him to wait another night or two, which he
did, and I got him a seat in the wings during my performances. The song he liked best was "We Parted on the Shore."
The chorus he shouted so loudly from his place in the wings
that I could scarcely hear myself singing it! He left for the
frozen north-west a few days later and I never heard from
him again.

CHAPTER FIFTEEN

I PLAY FOR ROYALTY

DURING this trip the American papers were once more exceedingly kind to me. Had I paid thousands and thousands of dollars I could not have secured a tenth part of the publicity they gave me. This is where my lucky star has always come to my aid. Quite apart from any quality of freshness and originality which may have been in my "act," the U. S. A. press helped to make me a public character. If I was asked to visit the Mayor in his civic parlour there was a column about it next morning. If I attended a Caledonian function of any kind the fact was reported—with photographs of me in my kilt shaking hands and smiling my broadest smile. If I went to a hospital ward and entertained the inmates, the youngest child in the place was "introduced" to me and again the flashlight brigade was in action to a man! I honestly never asked for all this publicity and I do not think Will Morris had much to do with it either at that time. Later, of course, he pulled all sorts of stunts in subsequent tours and I remember that I used to become thoroughly tired of the way he worked me quite apart from my stage business. But during this first trip under his wing both press and public seemed to lionize me of their own accord. Indeed at the end of the fourteen weeks I was glad to get back again to Britain for some rest and recreation.

So my career went on for several years. I would play a few months at home filling old contracts and making new ones—at prices which made the managers take deep breaths as they nervously attached their names—and then would whisk off to the States for three, four, or six months according to how I could arrange releases from my engagements in England. Often I had to pay sweetly for the privilege of postponing some of my bookings. Tom and Foster generally carried through these negotiations between them and that combination of Scot and Jew achieved marvellous results even in cases where I had sorrowfully made up my mind that parleying was useless. While Tom put over the rough stuff—and no man ever had a servant so absolutely devoted to his master's interests as I have had in Tom Vallance— Foster provided the oil of suavity—the "smoosh." Naturally the British managers hated to have any of their Lauder dates interfered with but most of them had begun to realize that it was better to have me for a friend than an enemy and so they made possible for me my now yearly trips to America. Not only so but the more discerning of them actually agreed to substantial increases of salary when I did fill in dates for them. A few days ago I met my old friend Sir Walter de Freece at a dinner in London and he was reminding me of an incident in this connection which made me laugh very heartily.

"Don't you remember, Harry," he said, "coming up to my office one day with a hank of red flannel round your neck and coughing as if the tomb was waiting for you? You wanted to postpone certain engagements in the Midlands which you had with my firm so that you could get away to America sooner than you otherwise would have done. There were two weeks' bookings in between my dates and I asked you what you were going to do about them. 'Oh, I can't postpone these,' you replied. 'I'm getting twice the money there that you're paying me.' And don't you remember how your cough vanished immediately when I began to speak about doubling your contract-price?" Sir Walter's story was not strictly true but there was enough accuracy in it to make me chuckle and offer to buy him a drink—of lemonade.

In the New Year season of 1910-11, I played another

Glasgow pantomine. That was an ever-memorable engagement for me because on the opening night I sang "Roamin' in the Glomin'" for the first time. If "I Love a Lassie" had been a great success under similar circumstances five years before this new lyric was a triumph. It captivated the public ear as no other song of mine has ever done—or will do until I come to sing "Flower o' the Heather." I had kept it up my sleeve for a year or two before producing it. I rehearsed it ten thousand times; I worked on it every day and often in my bed at night. I tried a dozen different costumes before I decided how I would dress for it. I studied each and every syllable of the words, every note and intonation of the music. The song was an obsession with me for months and months. I remember crossing on the *Lusitania* once with Lord Northcliffe and among the many interesting things this amazing man told me was a little story I have never forgotten. It was about a small shoemaker who invented the tags for bootlaces and made a fortune out of his notion. "How did you come to hit on the idea of putting steel points to the ends of laces?" Lord Northcliffe asked the shoemaker on meeting him many years afterwards. "By thinking of nothing else than boot laces for twenty years!" replied the inventor.

Well, I thought about nothing else than this song from the evening, a year or two previously; the title came suddenly to my mind. I had been out strolling in the cool of a fine summer night near my house at Dunoon. Every now and then I happened across a couple of lovers linked close together as they slowly "dandered" along the road to Inellan in the gathering dusk. They were oblivious to everything save the sweet nothings they whispered into each other's ears. The words of Burns came back to me as I passed first one pair and then another:

If heaven a draught of heavenly pleasure spare,
One cordial in this melancholy vale
'Tis when a loving, youthful, modest pair
In other's arms breathe out the tender tale
Beneath the milk-white thorn that scents the evening gale.

There they go, bless them! I said to myself. The old, old story. The ever new, entrancing story. What a perfect night, what a picturesque road, for love-making! No time so sweet for amorous dalliance as in the gloaming. Roaming in the gloaming! Suddenly I stopped dead. Roamin' in the Gloamin'. If ever a phrase deserved a song this did! What a title for a love lyric! Instead of going home I went up the hill behind Laudervale and hewed out a rough verse and chorus. Next day I had the song complete, words and melody, but months and months elapsed before I had all the "trimmings"—the patter, the expressions of the face, the essential etceteras—just to my liking. I tell you all this about "Roamin' in the Gloamin'" because people in every corner of the world seem to like it best of all my purely love songs and have asked me how I came to hit upon such a simple but eternally appealing theme.

In September, 1909, I had the great honour of my first Royal command performance. Curiously enough I was playing at the old Paragon, in the Mile-End Road, London, when the royal communication reached me so that the situation was evolved of a Scotsman singing to Jews—practically all the Paragon patrons were drawn from the ancient race—being commanded to sing before our King at one of the oldest and most noble palaces in the country. King Edward was on a visit to Lord and Lady Savile at Rufford Abbey. The host and hostess suggested to his majesty that perhaps he would like to be entertained by a leading artiste one evening during his visit. "Tell Harry Lauder to come and sing to us!" said King Edward. So down I went to Rufford Abbey, taking my son John with me as accompanist. We were most hospitably received by Lady Savile to whom I submitted my programme. In her turn she submitted it to King Edward. It contained a list of my songs and I had imagined that perhaps his majesty would indicate those numbers he would like to hear. Imagine my astonishment

when her ladyship returned with the Royal command that I
had "just to begin at the beginning of the list and his majesty
would tell me when to stop!"

My concert took place in what seemed to me to be one
of the greatest underground vaults of the turreted castle.
As there was a big house party at the Abbey for Doncaster
Races the audience numbered forty or fifty people. The King
sat well forward in the "Stalls" beside his host and hostess;
near them were many lords and ladies and other members
of the British aristocracy while in the rear seats were gathered the officials, esquires, lacquays, butlers, footmen, and
maidservants down to—I presume—the humble dishwashers
and stable grooms. There was a nice little stage with a piano
in one corner to which John tremblingly advanced when Lady
Savile gave us the signal to begin. I began with "I Love a
Lassie," went on with "Tobermory," "We Parted on the
Shore," "Stop Yer Ticklin', Jock!" and before I knew
where I was, so to speak, I had sung half a dozen songs. But
still there was no indication from the great personage in
the "front of the house" that he had had enough. So I just
went on to sing every song that I had jotted down on the list,
ten in all, and ending with "When I Get Back Again to
Bonnie Scotland." That number finished I went to the footlights, bowed several times and nodded to John to leave the
piano. "And that's all I can sing tonight," I announced,
"because I have no more music with me!" As a matter of
fact I was completely exhausted.

A few minutes later I was having a rub-down in the
dressing-room when a Royal equerry came to say that his
majesty wanted to see me. "Like this?" I asked jocularly,
indicating the state of nakedness in which I was at the
moment. The official laughed, said he would explain to the
King and that perhaps his majesty would wait for me. He
did so—and I can truthfully say that I am one of the few
men in the world who ever kept a King waiting! A few

minutes afterwards I was making my obeisance to his majesty and he was pleased to tell me that he had thoroughly enjoyed my performance as well as the playing of my son at the piano. King Edward was not only a great monarch but he was a man through and through.

I have also sung to King George and Queen Mary several times. The first occasion was when, as Prince and Princess of Wales, they were visiting an East-end district of London for some charitable object. A special concert was organized in the local town hall and I was one of the stars asked to assist. Later, when they had succeeded to the throne, they came to hear me at the Palace Theatre, London and only three years ago I was commanded to give a special performance at Balmoral Castle, that comparatively small but beautiful royal residence on lovely Deeside. Their majesties were exceedingly gracious to Lady Lauder and myself and gave us, amongst other mementoes of the occasion, two handsomely framed photographs, each of them autographed. They are on the piano in my drawing-room at Laudervale and, needless to say, I hold these photographs in very high esteem.

Writing about my meetings with British royalty reminds me of an altogether unique incident which occurred at the Palace Theatre the night King George and Queen Mary came to see my performance. Mr. George Ashton, the well-known London concert agent, who usually manages all such outings on behalf of British royalty, came round to the dressing-room and said that their majesties desired to have a chat with me in the Royal box. Of course I went up at once and remained with the King and Queen for perhaps seven or ten minutes. They were keenly interested in my American experiences for one thing and for another they asked me all about my songs, how I got the ideas for them, and how long I practised them. On making my way back to the dressing-room Mr. Ashton appeared in the corridor and with him was the Duke of Connaught. I was introduced to his royal highness and was standing speaking to him when Ashton moved off up the corridor. "Well, good-night, George," I shouted after him, "and good-luck!" Before the words left my mouth the King had emerged into the corridor from his box. With a broad smile on his face he turned in my direction and cried out, "And good-night and good-luck to you, Harry!" I was overwhelmed with confusion at the awful thought that I might be held as taking jocular liberties with the King-Emperor and stood riveted to the spot. But King George went off laughing very heartily at his own joke.

The Prince of Wales I have had the honour of meeting several times. In fact we are quite good friends. I have had him in my dressing room more than once. He is a splendid fellow and easily the most popular young man in Britain— aye, in the wide world. No wonder he is such a favourite wherever he goes for there is absolutely no "swank" in his make-up. Sunny-natured, with great freedom of manner and devoid of every semblance of hauteur, he has won the love and affection of the common people as no prince has ever done in the history of our land. Over in the States, too, he is just as big a success; I always say that we ought to send him across the Atlantic for a few months every year. He would do more good in the glorious cause of Anglo-American friendship than a dozen ambassadors no matter how skilfully chosen! Once the Prince came to the London Hippodrome when I was "on the Bill" there. It was at a time when rumours were unusually rife in London as to his forthcoming engagement and naturally everybody was dying to know just who the lucky girl was. He sat in a box and was so enthusiastically entering into the evening's fun that before I left the stage he cried out, "I Love a Lassie, Harry!" joining with others in the audience in the request for this old favourite. Quick as lightning I looked up at him and replied, "Yes, I know you do, but we all want to know who she is!" The people rocked with merriment while his royal highness also lay back and laughed heartily. Once when I was speaking to him privately I expressed the hope that he would follow the excellent example of his brother the Duke of York and marry a Scottish bride. "I might do worse, Harry!" was all he would commit himself to. Amongst my collection of twisted sticks which I use in my different character studies is one brought home from Japan by his royal highness specially for presentation to myself. When the Prince saw this stick out there he said, "I must take it home to Harry Lauder!" And he did.

After an unusually long engagement in the States I was entertained at a welcome-home banquet in London. Lord Dewar was the chief man behind the scenes in arranging this function and he himself took the chair. As usual he made a most witty speech the key-note of which was that Harry Lauder and Dewar's whisky were the greatest cementers of Anglo-American friendship. As an after-dinner speaker I think I would rather listen to Lord Dewar than any other man in the world, although an old United States Consul in London, a gentleman by the name of Griffiths, once had the reputation of running him very hard. Lord Dewar is an unfailing mine of wit and wisdom whenever he gets on his feet. I have seen and heard dozens of London audiences rock with laughter at his brilliant epigrams and quaint, sardonic philosophy. He has just the slightest impediment in his speech—it is not that exactly but rather a mannerism of hissing certain words—which makes his utterance all the more attractive. Not one of the ordinary tricks of the orator is exploited by Lord Dewar; he makes his points by sheer intellectual ability and by a sense of humour unsurpassed in any living man.

It is one of the greatest pleasures of my life that I am on terms of intimate personal friendship with his lordship. I often go down for a week-end to his wonderful country seat in Sussex where he has hundreds of acres given over entirely to what I call his menagerie. There are farms wholly devoted to horses, poultry, goats, and pigs, kennels for greyhounds, lofts for pigeons, ponds full of water-fowl; you could spend a week at East Grinstead and never see half of the animals within its borders! There must be thousands of them—and every one thoroughbred. There is no room on Lord Dewar's estate for any horse, cow, dog, or fowl of low degree! They are the aristocrats of the British animal and feathered world. Perhaps the favourite of all this multifarious collection in the eyes of their owner is the sultan of the racing stud, Abbot's Trace. This horse was leading in the Derby of his year when he fell coming up the home straight after showing terrific speed for fully a mile. Everybody thought he was dead but he got on his feet after all the other horses had passed him and walked back to the paddock. His owner was bitterly disappointed for he thought "the Trace" was sure to win the Blue Ribbon of the English turf. Trainers and other owners told Lord Dewar that his horse was no good and strongly advised him to sell Abbot's Trace. That he would ever be a famous sire was a proposition they laughed to scorn. But his noble owner had faith in the horse. He kept him because he loved him! And his belief in the quality of the old horse has been more than justified for his sons and daughters won more races last year than the progeny of any other sire, including some of the most important races in the calendar. Even in America a son of Abbot's Trace heads the list of winning racehorses down Kentucky way. Nothing gives Lord Dewar so much delight as to note that an Abbot's Trace colt or filly has again caught the judge's eye. Not even the report that America was giving up prohibition would please him better than to see one of his old favourite's sons winning a future Derby.

His lordship once played a very mean trick on me. Admiring his pigeons one day at East Grinstead I threw out the suggestion that a few of the lovely birds would look very nice flying round my eaves and turrets at Glen Branter, the West Highland estate I bought just before the war. His lordship said he would be delighted to send me a pair of his very best birds.

"In case you may forget," I replied pawkily, "I'll just take them with me; I am going up to Scotland tomorrow." So the birds were put in a basket there and then and next day they travelled with me to the north. I put them in a beautiful "dookit" which I had ordered by telegram to be prepared for them. But the moment they were given their liberty they disappeared. They were homing pigeons and were back at Lord Dewar's place before he got my letter complaining bitterly of the joke he had played on me. That's the kind of present one Scot gives to another!

Many are the good stories told about Lord Dewar. All sporting Britain was chuckling a few weeks ago over a letter he wrote to one of the racing papers. A correspondent had been taking him to task for naming so many of his horses Abbot's Smile, Abbot's Remorse, Abbot's Speed, Abbot's Frown, etc. It simply led to hopeless confusion on the part of backers, said the correspondent, and was quite as bad as the situation which evolved on the English turf some years ago when a famous sire named Bachelor's Button had a hundred sons and daughters running under the name of Bachelor's This or That. In his reply to the complaint Lord Dewar admitted the confusion but neatly urged that surely an Abbot had as much right to boast of his progeny as a Bachelor!

At a recent big London function Lord Dewar found himself seated next to a very pretty girl with the hyphened surname of Porter-Porter. Whether his lordship had not caught the double name or was disinclined to use it I don't know but the story goes that after being addressed as Miss Porter several times the young lady turned tartly to Lord Dewar and pointed out that, "my name, if you please, is

Porter-Porter with a hyphen!" "Ah!" swiftly retorted his lordship, "just as mine is Dewar-Dewar with a syphon!"

When Will Rogers—whose unofficial letters from Europe to the President of the United States were to my mind, the most amusing things I ever read—was in London some months ago it was the aim of dinner promoters to get Lord Dewar and Rogers on the same "bill." The result was a duel of wits unexcelled in the history of after-dinner oratory on this side of the Atlantic. They said the most cruel and disgraceful things about each other but in such clever language that the diners were convulsed with laughter. At one function where Lord Dewar had first innings he frankly asserted that the first time he heard Rogers he was convinced that the man was not "all there" but later in the evening Will completely turned the tables by stating that the first time he heard Dewar speaking in public he was certain that "this lordship bird" was "soused to the ears!" Unluckily for the entertainment of London society Will Rogers had to return to the States after a very brief visit and the battle between the two wits is suspended—temporarily only, it is hoped.

CHAPTER SIXTEEN

THE FIRST YEARS OF THE WAR

LOOKING back on the years between 1907 and 1914 it seems to me now that they passed with amazing swiftness. My engagement book was full up with British and American bookings. Life, so far as I was concerned, was a perpetual scamper over the chief towns of England, Scotland, and Ireland, and then off again to the States for another long tour. It is quite true that my bank-book was swelling in corresponding ratio to my engagement-book but while this fact gave me intense pleasure I was often oppressed with a feeling of horror when I realized that every week of my life for years ahead was irrevocably fixed and ordained. I had no time for holidays. If I got an occasional week-end at Lauderdale in Dunoon, or at Glen Branter on the shores of Loch Eck, Argyllshire—the Highland estate I now owned but seldom saw—it was as much as I could fit in. Of course the ocean trips to and from America were as good as vacations but I did miss that fine feeling that comes to most men and women once or twice a year—the exhilarating thought that now, for a week or a fortnight, they can cast care to the winds and thoroughly enjoy their holidays. More than once I tried hard to get released from dates on both sides of the Atlantic, but it was no good—managers' plans are made a long way ahead; I was a slave for whom there was never a respite.

Sometimes I fell to hating my life with a fierce hatred. What had I done that I should thus be kept at the grindstone, driven and dragooned, at home and abroad, week after week, month after month, year after year? For more than ten years I had had no home life worth speaking of.

Nance certainly went with me to America every time and she was an unfailing pillar of support and encouragement. Without her loving care and comradeship I must have kicked over the traces altogether and torn my contracts to tatters. I think John had a lot to do with these occasional moods of mine. He had now gone up to Cambridge. Even when I was playing in London and the British provinces I saw very little of him. Occasionally he would run down in his car for an evening or a week-end but I was always so full up with business that it seems to me now we never had the good times together that a father and a son ought to have had. I was proud of the progress he was making at college. His intention was to take his degree as a Bachelor of Music. He had everything that a boy could desire because by this time I was a comparatively rich man and my potential earning power was very great. But, as I have said; I was leading a slave's life. I was not my own master. True it is that the fascination of my stage work held me constantly in thrall. Whenever I pranced on from the wings to begin my act the world was wholly blotted out; private thoughts and reflections, resentments, longings—all were forgotten in the glare of the footlights. The applause of the people, the sense of personal mastery over the emotions of crowded audiences, the feeling of playing on the heart-strings of men and women as on an instrument—here are the "hooks" of steel that keep the artiste bound to the theatre through all the nights and all the years. Reaction comes only during the day. Over and over again during one or other of my American tours I have sent for Morris and told him point-blank that I was packing-up, that all the dollars in the United States Treasury could not keep me a day longer away from my home and my boy. I saw him in daily association with his own fine son, young Will, and my heart cried out for John. But of course I always lost in these bouts with my manager; he had the most

wonderful way of soothing me and encouraging me to
"Carry On!"

"Sure, Harry," Will would say in his quiet style, "I'll
cancel everything after this week. But don't forget that you
have to breakfast with the President on such-and-such a date.
And remember you have arranged to meet Henry Ford and
see his Detroit plant the week after!" Or it would be an
appointment with some senator, or a game of golf with
George Low, or a day at Congress, or something equally fascinating to which he knew I had been keenly looking forward. No matter how home-sick I might have been Will
Morris always had his own way!

And, these infrequent temperamental storms apart, I
must admit that I always found each successive visit to the
States refreshing and invigorating to a degree. Remember
that by the time of which I am writing I had come to know
the country from coast to coast. I had made innumerable
friends from the highest in the land down to the humblest
citizen. I had received the freedom of practically every large
city. I had been entertained by all the leading clubs, societies,
and associations. Great organizations like the Rotary clubs
and Kiwanis had invited me to their weekly meetings in
every State in the Union. I had visited every historic spot,
been shown over every industrial plant, was now perhaps
better acquainted with the national life and characteristics of
the people than millions claiming citizenship under the Stars
and Stripes. By and by in these memoirs I propose to give
you some brief impressions of the great Americans I have
met and talked with from Teddy Roosevelt down to the
political and industrial leaders of the present time. I will
also, with the editor's permission, recount some of the more
amusing adventures and experiences that I have had during
my twenty years' touring of the United States. But these
impressions and stories must fall in their proper place. At
present I feel that I should be getting on with my roamin's

in other parts of the world and to the War years which held so much of action and excitement for all of us and so much of woe for many of us.

The question of my visiting Australia had frequently been broached to me and I had actually agreed to the terms of an exceedingly handsome offer put up to me as far back as 1911. But it was not until three years later that I was free to set sail for the island-continent. This I did from San Francisco in February, 1914. The long sail over the blue Pacific was an enchanting experience to me. I do not suppose there is a boy or man in the wide world who has not dreamed, at one time or another, of the South Sea Islands, of coral reefs and waving palm-trees, of moonlight nights and melody under the Southern Cross. I did very often as a wee boy. And here was I, the poor half-timer in Gordon Flax Mill, the toiling miner in the coal pits of Lanarkshire, having my dreams realized—I was indeed sailing away into the seas, and to the islands, of romance. I have made the same voyage several times since then but have never quite recaptured the sensations which marked my first venturing upon those wonder seas of the West.

We arrived at Sydney on a glorious morning. As we slowly sailed up the magnificent harbour—surely the noblest "home of ships" in all the world—every vessel flagged me a welcome or blew a Cock-a-Doodle-Do on her siren. But if I felt flattered by the reception given me in the harbour itself what can I say about the warmth of the welcome accorded me by the people of Sydney? Had I been the discoverer of Australia returning after fifty years, to see how the people were faring I could not have been received with greater acclaim. The quays were crowded, the main streets were lined, bands were playing, the Mayor and the members of the Corporation were on duty to hand me, metaphorically, the keys of Sydney and of Australia. It was all very wonderful. I felt, as I have always felt on such occasions, that

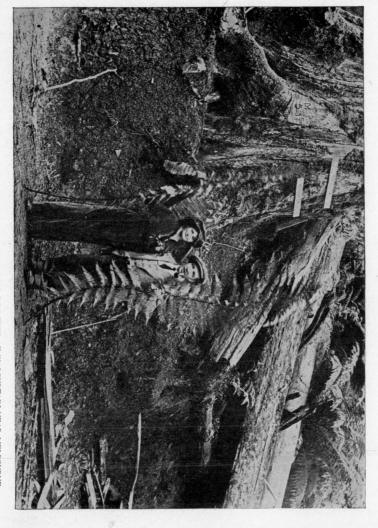

SIR HARRY AND LADY LAUDER IN FRONT OF AN ENORMOUS GUM TREE AT WARBURTAIN NEAR MELBOURNE

I was wholly unworthy of demonstrations so enthusiastic, so general, so spontaneous. Again, of course, the expatriated Scotties were prominent in the welcome; I have never been under any misapprehension as to the publicity value of my own kith and kin throughout the world. The fiery cross of the "clansmen" is as potent today to rally the Macdonalds, the Macintoshes, the Macgregors, the Duncans, the Tamsons, as ever it was in the days of the Young Pretender!

They gave me a fine banquet at Farmer's Stores the following evening. I sang "Roamin' in the Gloamin'" but though there were vociferous demands for an encore I told them that my programme would be continued on Easter Saturday night at the Theatre Royal and at the usual charges for admission! I played a solid month at Sydney that first visit. There was never an empty seat in the house. Afterwards I went to Melbourne, played the same number of weeks under the same happy conditions and subsequently made the pleasant (and extremely profitable) acquaintance of the people of Adelaide, Brisbane, and other towns. I also went down to New Zealand for six weeks. Here I got an absolutely amazing welcome. You must remember that the folks in New Zealand are more Scottish than the Scots themselves; their lovely islands are known as "the other Scotland down under." I had some gorgeous trout-fishing in New Zealand. That country I should describe as an angler's paradise. Many and many a fine basket of the speckled beauties I have landed down Invercargill way with my friend Donald Macdonald and some day I am going back there not to work but to fish all day long—and all night, too, if they're rising!

I was happier during this trip to Australia than I had been for a long time. It had been arranged that John was to come out and join us for a long holiday immediately after Cambridge had closed down for the summer vacation. He was within a few days' sail of Australia when we got back from New Zealand. And his mother and I could scarcely contain ourselves for joy over the thought that he would soon be with us. I cried like a child when he stepped off the ship looking bronzed and well after his voyage and bigger and more manly than when I had seen him about a year previously. His training as a subaltern in the territorial regiment of the Argyll and Sutherland Highlanders had evidently done him good, I told myself. Our greetings over, the first thing he said to me was, "What's the news from home, Dad? The outlook is pretty bad, don't you think?" He referred, of course, to the war clouds then gathering thick and foreboding over the political horizon in Europe. I replied that everybody was trusting the situation would be clarified very soon; my own view was that a European war was unthinkable. In any case the war, if it did come, would not immediately affect Britain.

"Don't make any mistake, Dad!" said John quietly but more seriously than I had ever known him speak. "If it comes to war we are in it up to the hilt. And in that case I'll be re-called at once. Rather hard lines," he concluded, "after looking forward to a jolly good time with you and Mum out here!"

John's reading of the war situation was more accurate than mine. He arrived on the last day of July, war was declared between Britain and Germany on August fourth (my birthday as it happened) and next day a cable arrived for John from the British War Office ordering him to rejoin his regiment at once. He sailed for home by the first available steamer. The next time we saw him was at Bedford six or seven months later just before leaving for the French front with the Highland Division.

A sincere and affectionate friendship which I had cemented in Australia stood my wife and me in good stead during this anxious period. I refer to E. J. Carroll, now one of the best-known impresarios in Australia and Great

Britain but at that time chiefly prominent because of his film interests in Queensland and for his association with the famous firm of Tait Brothers. It was Ted Carroll who had come over to London several years previously and prevailed on me to sign a contract with the Taits. He was my "guide, philosopher, and friend" throughout that first tour. To know Ted Carroll is to love him. Genial and gentle, with a simple exterior masking extraordinary ability and foresight, slow of speech but wise in counsel. "E. J." is the type of man one trusts implicitly from the moment one meets him. He is a credit to the theatrical profession. He is as well-known in London now as in Australia. With the exception of my American work Mr. Carroll has managed me in all my Dominion and foreign tours during the past thirteen years and he will continue to do so until the end. I could tell you a lot more about E. J. Carroll, his beautiful character, his generosity, the esteem in which he is held by my profession but I am sure I have already said far more about him than will please him. He cheered me up when John's mother and I were sad, and made our first trip to Australia, in spite of our fears and occasional fits of depression, a memorable and highly delightful time.

I had a long list of bookings to play in the States on the way home, commencing at 'Frisco and zig-zagging all over the country, so it was not until the spring of 1915 that we set foot once more in England. As soon as ever we could get up to Bedford we did so and during the next month or two we saw a lot of John and his officer friends of the Fifty-first Division. This division was almost unique in the British Army. Being a territorial unit officers and men were all known to each other; apart from the formal military discipline they were more like companies of brothers and pals. The Argylls mostly all came from Argyll or Stirlingshires, the Black Watch from Perth, Forfar, and Fifeshires, the Gordons from Aberdeen and Banffshires, and so on. There were companies, or sections, entirely made up of Dunoon men, of Stirling men, of Dundee men, of St. Andrews men; districts and towns were thus closely associated and it all made for *esprit de corps* (the only French phrase I really understand!) not only in training but in the fighting days that lay ahead. I knew hundreds of the officers and men and always felt proud that our boy belonged to such a fine division. They were all kilted and their regimental music was the pipes. Man, but they must have looked grand as they marched through France to the front line! I often wished to God that I could join up with them. But I was over age and, for another thing, their ranks were closed to all but territorial soldiers.

Later in the war, my friend Willie Blackwood joined up and was lucky enough to get posted to the Fifty-first. Often, since the war, I have listened to Blackwood for hours as he told quaint, amusing, or tragic stories of his army days with the famous "H. D." (Highland Division) in France. One of his senior officers was his brother-in-law's foreman porter in peace days; his own batman was an insurance agent who had insured his life some years previously. A sergeant in his company was a Dundee schoolmaster with a string of letters after his name. His adjutant was the shoemaker from whom he bought his boots in private life. The driver of the mess-cart was one of the most accomplished architects in the midlands of Scotland. His major was a furniture dealer in Stirling. The colonel was a lawyer in Perth—"dear auld Wullie Grey," as Blackwood calls him. Of Colonel Grey conducting a Court Martial against one of his own "boys" Blackwood tells a story which always makes me chuckle with merriment. The soldier's crime is not heinous but of sufficient seriousness to warrant an inquiry. After hearing all the evidence the colonel turns to the culprit and delivers himself as follows:

"I'm real sorry, Jamie Broon (or whatever his name

was) to see ye in this disgraceful poseetion before me. Ye maun mind that this is no the toon o' Perth ye're in but France and that there's a war on. What wad yer faither, dooce man, think if I were to write an' tell him that ye had been misbehavin' yersel' oot here? I ken yer faither fine an' it wad break the auld mon's hert!"

By this time, of course, the offending soldier is reduced to tears and he replies in sobbing accents, "Dinna dae that, Maister Grey, for God's sake. I'm awfu' sorry for what I've dune but I swear I'll no come afore ye again. Declare tae God, Maister Grey!"

And so, with an admonition, the kindly territorial colonel —the father as well as the commander of his men—dismisses the case!

Blackwood always asserts that the only trouble the officers of the Highland Division had to face was to prevent the men fighting among themselves when they were not fighting the Germans. One of the most bloodthirsty affrays he saw in France, he recounts, took place behind the line near Bapaume, one Hogmanay night—the last night of the year and a special festival evening with all Scots either in peace or war. Some of the transport boys had secretly laid in a large amount of rum for the due celebration of the occasion. The proceedings were marked at first with tremendous cordiality and conviviality all round but about midnight an argument arose as to whether Aberdeen or Dundee was the better town to live in. Words led to blows and soon a miniature battle was in progress. The Aberdeen-Dundee disputants were putting up a capital show, so good that others thought they would like to join in. Only when casualties began to be serious was the guard called out and the battle finished. Next morning the regimental postman appeared at the officers' quarters with his head swathed in bandages and, as he handed out the letters, Lieutenant Blackwood asked him if he had been "in the scrap last night." "I was that, sir!" proudly replied the postman, "an' it was certainly a grand fecht. But I wish I knew the —— that got away wi' my left ear!"

Before going to the front John got an occasional leave and we spent several week-ends together at Glen Branter where I was building a house for him on the estate. He was now engaged to be married to the sweetheart of his boyhood, Miss Mildred Thomson, whose father was a big warehouse proprietor in London. John himself never seemed to doubt that he would come through the war all right but often I had a presentiment in the other direction. So many thousands of our best and bravest young men were being "a' wede awa'" that it was too much to hope my boy would escape. Naturally I did not mention my fears to John who, for his part was buoyantly looking forward to going "over there" with his beloved men.

I was on the Atlantic bound once more for America when John and his Highlanders sailed to France. Morris had arranged a very long and strenuous tour. After my opening weeks in New York my wife and I practically lived on a train for six months. Now that I come to think of it I must have spent a good few years of my life on American trains! And a man could live in many worse places, believe me. In the early days I had the *Riva* Saloon which President Roosevelt used during his presidential travels. Other well-known people who had had the privilege of touring in it before me were Sarah Bernhardt and Adelina Patti. Later I had other parlour cars placed at my disposal. Generally a "Harry Lauder Special" train consisted of three coaches, a baggage car, a Pullman sleeping car for my company, and the parlour car for myself, my wife, and Mr. Morris. These trains ran unchanged all over the North American continent. The original railway company took over all arrangements for each tour. And to the credit of the American Railroads be it said that in twenty years, and in the covering of many hundreds of thousands of miles, I have only once been in an accident.

That was at Buffalo where we were run into by another "special," and very nearly all sent to kingdom come.

Some of the train servants travelled with me on many successive trips. There was one, a big black fellow, named Tom, who was a magnificent cook and the best maker of waffles I ever came across. I must have eaten many thousands of black Tom's waffles. One night my own Tom asked the other Tom if he would like to go to the theatre and see "Big Boss," perform—meaning me. "Sutt'nly, Massa Tom," said the cook. So white Tom got a ticket for him at some town out west. On returning to the *Riva* late that night Vallance asked the black fellow how he had enjoyed my act. "Fust-class, Massa Tom, fust-class!" he exclaimed, "but I'se mighty glad he don't break his damn neck when he slips ever so high and come down ker-wallop!" The criticism of my performance so puzzled Tom that he began to make inquiries. It appeared that our cook had gone to the theatre right enough, that the first "turn" was by a grotesquely attired acrobat who made comedy tumbles off chairs piled up almost to the flies, and that after seeing this act he left the theatre under the impression that he had seen "Big Boss" Harry Lauder!

This tour in 1915 is stamped in my memory by the fact that I did a lot of propaganda work on behalf of my country not only from the stage but at meetings arranged in many places so that I could tell the people why we were in the war and of the part we were playing in the conflict. All along, even in these early days, I felt convinced that the United States would have to come into the war sooner or later. I told Mr. Wilson so at the White House and I lost no opportunity of saying the same thing throughout the length and breadth of America. That America's position was exceedingly difficult I well realized. I was in a neutral country. There were millions of German sympathisers in the States, men and women of German or Austrian origin, Swedes and others

whose leanings were all on the side of the Black Eagle. Blood
is always thicker than water and I could not blame them.
But I knew that Britain's hands were clean, that we had
taken up the sword on behalf of what we deemed a righteous
cause and that we were draining our manhood in support of
an ideal. All this I told my audiences whenever I had the
chance. Sometimes my remarks were well received; sometimes they were not. Occasionally Will Morris was a bit
dubious of the wisdom of my almost fanatical speeches on
behalf of my country, not, let me say at once, because he
was not with me heart and soul but because he was frightened that I might get a bad break somewhere. Still I carried
on. At a great meeting in San Francisco in December '15, I
said, "You have got to come in and help us. America is part
and parcel of Britain in this fight. Your institutions and
your ideals march with ours. Your aspirations, your democ-
racy, your outlook on life are the twins of our own—you
cannot much longer stand aloof and see Europe plunged into
hell because a gang of junkers have pulled out their sabres
and sung a war-song proclaiming their determination to ride
rough-shod over all the nations of the earth!" Of course I
received many threatening letters and was repeatedly told
that I should stick to my legitimate business of the stage
without mixing it up with British propaganda offensive to
many citizens of the country in which I was touring as a
paid entertainer. At Pittsburgh one evening I was billed to
speak in one of the largest halls. After a most enthusiastic
meeting some friends—real Americans—and I were passing
by the newspaper offices where the war bulletins were being
shown in a dozen different languages. They were being
eagerly devoured by a motley crowd the vast proportion of
which could not speak English and whose sole idea of
America was that it was a country which had treated them
better than the lands they had been glad to leave. "What do
these people know about the rights or wrongs of the war?"

said one of my Pittsburgh friends bitterly. "They are not sufficiently interested in America to learn to speak its language." But many of this class of her citizens were only too keen, when the time came, to plot and scheme and work sedition against the country that had been kind enough to receive them into her great, generous bosom.

CHAPTER SEVENTEEN

"CARRY ON"

HOME again early in 1916 just in time to welcome John on his first leave from France and the trenches! Oh, but it was splendid to see the boy safe and sound and grown bigger and stronger than ever! He was now a captain, having been promoted several months before. We had a few days at the Glen together and spoke of the many things we would do "after the war." A list of provincial dates kept me as busy as usual and in the late autumn I went into my first Revue at the Shaftesbury Theatre, London. My first—and my last. "Three Cheers" was quite as good a show as most successful revues are but somehow I never felt myself thoroughly happy in it. My work as an artiste is too individual for revue. Ethel Levey and I had some excellent scenes in "Three Cheers" and one of the big hits in the piece was my war-song "The Laddies Who Fought and Won." This number sent the audience into hysterical enthusiasm at every performance; the chorus was always taken up and shouted vociferously. A company of Scots Guards in full uniform marched on to the stage at the finish of the song, the final scene, before the fall of the curtain, being most war-like and inspiring. I put my whole soul into the singing of this song. John was never out of my mind from the opening bars till the last—it was of him and his gallant boys of the Fifty-first I was singing. Yet, as I have said, I never was at happy ease in this revue. Often I had fits of the most violent depression. These were not altogether dissociated from the daily publication of tremendously long lists of British casualties. I dreaded to buy a newspaper. In the closing days of the year Nance went up to Scotland

196

SIR HARRY AND HIS SON, THE LATE CAPTAIN JOHN LAUDER, 8TH ARGYLL AND
SUTHERLAND HIGHLANDERS

to be beside her ain folks for that peculiarly Scottish festival.
I was left alone in London.

On Monday morning, the first day of 1917 I was handed
a telegram. My heart started to beat double-time. I could
not bring myself to open the telegram. I knew what it contained. God! the agonies I suffered that bright New Year's
morning. They cannot be written about. But hundreds of
thousands, aye, millions, of fathers and mothers will know
just what I passed through for many hours and for many
weeks. My only son. The one child God had given us.

"Captain John Lauder killed in action. Official.
War Office."

That was what the telegram said when I came to read
it. Then I noticed the post-mark. It was from Dunoon.
So Nance knew already! Brave soul, she had received the
information first and simply re-directed it on to me. Pulling
myself together I realized that my place was at Dunoon
with my boy's mother. Throughout the day many of my
personal friends called at the hotel and their presence and
kindly words of sympathy and encouragement kept me on
something of a level keel mentally and physically. Tom
Vallance, the boy's uncle, never left me for a moment and
he and I travelled up to Scotland by the midnight mail.
The meeting between Nance and myself next morning I
shall never forget. She was wonderful. Through her tears
her eyes shone with a brave light. For her there were no
hysterics, no frenzied outbursts against Fate—and God.
She was proud of John in death as she had been of him
in life. I was the weak individual that morning; she the
strong. And after we had prayed a little together, not
questioning His mysterious ways, but simply asking Him
for strength and comfort, we both felt slightly more resigned
to our terrible loss.

Had it not been for Nance and her mothering of me
at that time I think my professional career would have ended

with John's death. "We mustna forget, Harry," she would often say, "that you and I are only two amongst countless fathers and mothers who have made the same sacrifice as we have been called on to make! Think, Harry, of all the weeping mothers in Scotland and England and ower the seas every day of the war! There's hardly a house in Scotland where a bonnie laddie hasna been grat for by a father or mother some day or another since the struggle began. And think o' the fatherless bairns an' the stricken wives an' the auld folks wi' naebody left to fend for them and care for them!" Thus did John's mother carry more than her own load during that day or two of our sad reunion in the silent house on Clydeside.

The London Revue "Three Cheers" was closed down on account of my trouble for the first three days of the year. Had I merely consulted my own inclinations I would, of course, have immediately cut adrift from all stage work. But to replace me in the Revue was impossible. I had either to return and resume my part in the show or see it suddenly disbanded with all that this meant in the way of financial loss to hundreds of people. My wife said I ought to go back. Tom pointed out that I had a duty to the more poorly paid members of the profession associated with me in the production—loss of work at this season of the year would for them be little short of disaster. A letter from one of John's brother officers telling us how he died decided my line of action. The last words my boy uttered were "Carry on!" I resolved that I also would carry on!

How I managed to get through that ordeal on the Thursday evening God only knows. I remember very little about it and what I do remember seems to be part of a terrible dream. They tell me that the house was crowded to suffocation. That the feeling of tenseness both in front and behind was almost unbearable. That I dressed for my part as usual and stood in the wings for a few minutes before the orchestra played the first notes of my opening song, a simple little love-lyric called "I Love My Jean." That I faltered then and turned away as from an impossible task but that Tom caught hold of me, wheeled me round and whispered in my ear, "Remember John's words, Harry—Carry On!" The next few minutes I do most vividly recollect. I braced my shoulders and ran on to the stage. For just a moment the people were silent. Then they burst into a tornado of cheering standing up in all parts of the house and shouting the most loving and affectionate and encouraging remarks to the poor Jack Point who was trying to do his duty while his heart was breaking. After cheering they started to cry —there can have been few dry eyes in the Shaftesbury Theatre at that moment. All this I remember. What happened afterwards is not so clear in my mind. But they say I sang my first song as well and as brightly as ever I sang in my life even if I did fall helplessly into Tom's arms on coming off the stage.

I must have made a tremendous effort to keep going during the rest of the performance. I am told that I did not miss a cue or a line or a gesture all the way through. But I knew that the final scene would get me on the raw! The big scene in the last act of the revue was my song "The Laddies Who Fought and Won." As Fate would have it I had written two lines in the refrain of this song picturing what would happen at the end of the war:

> When we all gather round the old fireside
> And the fond mother kisses her son ——

I knew I would never be able to sing these words. It was unthinkable. The song went all right so far as the verses were concerned, but each time I came to these lines in the chorus I choked—I tried hard but it was impossible. The music went on, the Scots Guards and the audience sang the lines and I was able to recover myself sufficiently to

continue. I have an idea that at the finish of the performance
there was another big emotional outburst on the part of the
people in front. They tell me so. But after I had led the
singing of "God Save the King" I fainted. You may ask
why I chose to recall all these details about a night so sad,
so full of grief, so charged with personal drama. I do so
because I think it is only right and proper if I am to tell
the real story of my life in these memoirs. As a rule the
public only sees the successful side of the actor, or public
man anywhere, who has made good at his profession or in
his business. They see only the outward and visible signs
of his prosperity, his triumphs; they note only the approving
shouts and the worship of the multitude; too often do they
envy his riches, his popularity, his life all "spread in pleasant
places." My God, they ought to know what I suffered that
night and for many, many nights and weeks and months
afterwards!

Yes, I played in "Three Cheers" until the piece ended.
Nance came up to London. During the days we did a lot
of hospital work together. This took our minds off our
own trouble, for there's nothing like taking an interest in
the sorrows of others for assuaging your own. At least
that was our experience. In addition to singing to the
wounded in different hospitals all over London I spoke at
many functions on behalf of war charities or on the then
highly important topic of conserving food supplies. One
of the largest demonstrations held in London during the
war took place in Drury Lane Theatre. Lord Balfour of
Burleigh, the great Scottish nobleman, and I were the two
chief speakers and I remember how pleased I was to be told
by this wonderful veteran that my work for the wounded
and in the soldiers' camps all round London was much appreciated by the Government. When the revue at the Shaftesbury Theatre came off I made up my mind to enlist. Older
men than I had done so. But I didn't want home service

—if I joined up I wanted a guarantee that I would be sent
to the front! I broached the subject to more than one prominent man in the Government or at the War Office. There
would be no difficulty, I was told, about enlisting and there
would be even less in getting me a commission. But whenever I said that I wanted to go out and fight the enemy who
had killed my boy they simply laughed and told me I was
far too old for the trenches.

"Then, for God's sake," I replied, "if you won't let
me fight in the trenches let me go out and sing to the boys
in the trenches!" This idea was not pooh-poohed as the other
had been. There certainly was something in it, the big men
admitted. But for a long time I heard no more about my
highly original suggestion. I had only to say the word and
I could easily have done what many other prominent artistes
had been doing—constantly visiting the bases in France and
Belgium and there entertaining the thousands of men and
women engaged in base work or the wounded lying in the
hospitals. But I wanted to do something bigger. I was all
lit up now with this idea of singing to the boys who were
actually in the fighting line. I wanted to get right among
them, to see for myself what they were doing, how they
were doing it, to cheer them up and encourage them. And
perhaps, I secretly told myself, I might be able to visit my
own little hallowed spot of ground where John was sleeping.

For a long time I heard no more of this wonderful
scheme of mine. I knew that it had been put up to those
in supreme authority but as the weeks went past and I heard
nothing I gloomily decided that it had been turned down.
Nance and I went up to Scotland for a wee holiday among
the hills. We were both very ill and exhausted. We spent
our time between Laudervale and Glen Branter but both
places were too full of associations with John for us to be
anything else but thoroughly miserable. At every point and

at every turn we were reminded of the boy who was lying dead in France. There were his photographs, his guns, his fishing-rods, his horse, his billiard cue, his books, his music! And right over the road from Glen Branter was Invernoaden House all ready to receive him and his bonnie bride. I tell you we cried ourselves to sleep every night.

Then one day, at the end of May, came a letter from the War Office giving me my orders. My request had been agreed to. I was to visit the front with full permission to entertain the Scottish troops wherever they were. I was to be taken specially to those sectors of the British front where the Argyll and Sutherlands, the Black Watch, the Camerons, the Gordons and the Highland Light Infantry were operating. These names always make the blood of a Scot run faster for the hearing even in the "piping times of peace" but in the war years they were magic words to me and to "ilka son o' the heather." I knew how our Highland glens had been cleared to the last young man, how every town and village in Scotland had been drained to supply these famous regiments with the necessary man-power. Can you wonder if I felt like going across the Channel and hugging every kilted laddie to my heart?

Two intimate personal friends of my own had been selected to accompany us—James Hogge, a member of Parliament for one of the divisions of Edinburgh, whose work on behalf of the widows and orphans of fallen soldiers and sailors had won the admiration of the country, and the Reverend George Adam, at that time a prominent official in the Munitions Ministry, who had come home from his church in Montreal to lend a hand in the struggle. Better companions could not have been desired. "Jamie" Hogge and "Geordie" Adam and I have been through lots of "ploys" together but none half so interesting or memorable as our trip to the War Zone in 1917. On the boat which took us across the Channel we were christened "The Rev-

erend Harry Lauder, M.P.'s Party," and this cognomen
stuck to us all the time. I carried with me a small portable
piano and tens of thousands of packets of cigarettes. My
intention was to accompany my own songs where I could
not pick up a volunteer accompanist but I was not called
upon to strike a note on the instrument because there were
always more volunteers than I could find employment for.
The "fags" I thought would last me a week, giving a packet
to every Tommy I found short of a smoke, but they were
all distributed within a very few hours of our setting foot
in France! Had I taken a full ship-load the result would
have been the same.

Our party was put under the absolute command of a
smart young staff officer, Captain Godfrey, and he seldom
left us night or day during our tour. I gave my first concert
in the Casino at Boulogne, then being used as a base hospital.
All the wounded men able to crawl or be helped into one
of the largest wards attended the "show" and I have never
sung to a more enthusiastic audience. My heart was near
my mouth all the time I was singing but there wasn't a
dull face among that maimed and stricken assembly of
heroes. Next day we went "up the line" and our adventures
started in earnest. We were seldom far away from the
firing-line. We worked eastward to Albert and Arras and
down as far as Peronne, having many opportunities of seeing every phase of the soldiers' lives from the base right
up to the front-line trenches. We visited the infantry, the
artillery, and the transport and wherever it was a feasible
proposition I set up my portable piano and sang to officers
and men in the open-air, in rest camps, in dug-outs, in
old chateaux, ruined farms, tumble-down barns—everywhere. There was never any difficulty in getting an audience;
the news of my presence travelled like wild-fire and all
the chaps who could get off duty came post-haste to hear
Harry Lauder. I knew dozens and dozens of the men in

the Ninth, Fifteenth and Fifty-first Divisions. Old schoolmates in Arbroath and old miners from Hamilton and other
towns in the West Country came forward and greeted me;
at each halt it was like a reunion of good friends and
acquaintances.

Sometimes I gave as many as half-a-dozen concerts in
a day. The audiences varied from a hundred or two up to
several thousands. At Arras, for instance, which was one
of the great British centres in France, there must have been
at least five thousand men assembled in the twilight of a
soft June evening. That was a scene I shall never forget.
The ruins all around, soldiers densely packed in front of
me, behind, and to left and right, aeroplanes circling overhead to keep off prowling Jerries, my voice ringing out in
the verses of my songs and being drowned in the lusty and
spontaneous singing of the choruses. Occasionally a shell
would come whizzing overhead just to let us know that
there was a war on and that death was lurking near. I
remember finishing that concert in almost pitch darkness.
I must have sung a dozen or fifteen songs to the boys but
they were still anxious for more. There were calls for some
of the old favourites I hadn't included, and above the shouts
came a great voice which boomed, "I'm frae Aberfeldy,
Harry—for God's sake sing us 'The Wee Hoose 'Mang
the Heather!'" Such a request could not be ignored. I sang
the old lyric with its simple refrain:

> There's a wee hoose 'mang the heather,
> There's a wee hoose ow'er the sea,
> There's a lassie in that wee hoose
> Waiting patiently for me.
> She's the picture o' perfection,
> I wouldna' tell a lee;
> If ye saw her ye would love her
> Just the same as me.

And I'm thinking that many of the kilties who sang
the haunting chorus with me at Arras that night never
again saw the wee hoose or the lassie they had in mind

and that the lassie herself is still dreaming of a soldier's lonely grave overseas.

When we were at Arras we were told that several companies of one of the Highland regiments were holding a railway cut on the line between that town and Lens out of which latter place the Germans had just been driven. Would it be possible for me to go out and sing to them? they sent a messenger in to ask. Certainly, I replied, and as Captain Godfrey was willing that we should take any risk that was going we set off without more ado. We reached the railway cutting all right and soon had all the soldiers gathered round us. The place was literally honeycombed with shell-holes and dugouts—a pretty dreadful spot it seemed to me. But a cheerier crowd of Scotties you couldn't imagine. They gave me an exceedingly boisterous welcome. Our concert had not been started more than a few minutes when a shell came plump into the cutting and exploded with a shattering roar. I suddenly stopped short in the song I was singing; I felt queer in the pit of the stomach. After a little while I started again. But another shell followed, hitting a railway-bridge perhaps two hundred yards, or less, from where we were standing. "They've spotted us!" said the officer in charge. Sure enough a perfect rain of shells began to fall all around us. All thoughts of further singing left my mind and I turned and ran for the nearest dug-out into which I scrambled in a most undignified fashion. I was in my kilt and was wearing a tin helmet. The latter tilted off my head as I legged it for safety and Hogge and Adam afterwards told me that I was a most comical spectacle tearing down the cutting as hard as I could go with the tin helmet dangling down the side of my face. Hogge certainly reached the dug-out some minutes after I did, but the Reverend George was there when I arrived so I do not see that *he* was in a position to say how *I* looked!

A German aeroplane had evidently observed the concentration of the men for the concert and had signalled the position to one of the enemy batteries. For fully half an hour the "strafe" was kept up and I must here testify to the remarkably accurate hitting of the Germans composing that particular battery. There were no casualties on our side, although several of the shells fell very near our dug-out. How did I feel under shell-fire? you may ask. To be perfectly candid—horrible! I seemed to have no "middle register." I knew I had legs and a head but there was nothing in between. My main thought was not of death or injury but rather what would happen if a shell struck the dug-out and we were all buried beneath tons of earth and wood and iron. The soldiers in the dug-out with us were as cheery as crickets, laughing and joking and smoking—a group of them started to play cards. "Harry" said a brawny, hairy-legged sergeant from Dundee "dinna fash yersel'! If yer name's on a shell or a bullet you'll get it an' if it's no yer as safe as a bug in a rug!" But to say that this bit of soldier philosophy in any way steadied my nerves would be to tell a deliberate untruth. However, the din died down by and by and we sallied forth and concluded the concert without further interruption. The original audience was greatly added to by the presence of a large number of English and Irish and South African Tommies who had been bathing in the River Scarpe on the other side of the railway cutting and to whom the news of our presence had been carried. They did not wait to dress but came running up as they were born and lined up to hear my songs. I have had many weird audiences in my life in far-flung parts of the world but that was the only occasion I ever sang to hundreds of stark naked men! When I took my departure they used their shirts and other items of clothing to wave me a hearty farewell.

We were taken up to the historical Vimy Ridge and we

watched, from different battery positions, our soldiers making the German trenches uncomfortable. I actually fired one of the British guns myself. When I had more or less recovered from the tremendous shock of the discharge Hogge, who had a pair of field-glasses at his eyes, swore that a German was coming over No Man's Land bearing in one hand a white flag and in the other a cocoanut! I had, he said, hit the bull's eye!

At Auhigny was the rest camp of the Fifteenth Division made up of Scottish troops second only in reputation to the redoubtable Fifty-first, or Highland Division. We were billed to give a concert here, and again I had a most cordial reception. Later in the evening our party, with many of the Scottish officers on rest-leave, were invited to a picturesque old chateau occupied by a French lady and her daughter who had point-blank refused to abandon their home for some safer territory farther away from the war area. The beautiful drawing-room was lit by candles and it was crowded with officers in kilts of different tartans reminding me for all the world of a social gathering of Scottish chiefs during the '45 Rebellion. Any one of the younger officers present might conceivably have been Bonnie Prince Charlie. I sang several songs. The scene when I gave the final toast to "our brave hostess and her lovely daughter" will long live in my memory.

Before leaving France after a most interesting and fortifying experience with our soldier lads I was able, as I had hoped, to visit John's grave. My companions went with me as far as the little cemetery at Ovillers, on the Albert-Peronne Road. There, like the thoughtful and kindly men they are, they left me and I fought out my battle alone.

CHAPTER EIGHTEEN

THE WAR YEARS IN AMERICA

AFTER I had been to the front that first time—I went back on more than one occasion and carried out similar programmes—my mind was held by one supreme purpose. That was to aid my country and the Allies in every way possible. What I had been privileged to see behind the lines inflamed me with a tremendous zeal. So I came home to London and renewed my hospital work, my lecturing, and my visitations of the military encampments with as much energy as I could throw into the task. Yet anything I could do seemed so small, so ineffective, compared with the stupendous job our men were carrying on in France, that I again began to chafe for a more active share in the fight.

I do not think it would be advisable on my part just to say how the suggestion came about—war diplomacy is a ticklish thing to deal with even ten years after the event—but a few months after my return from France I was approached to know whether I would go to America and tell the people there the simple story of what I had seen in the war zone. Not as a propagandist, purely and simply, but as an actual observer. America, it was well known, had been over-run by all kinds of special pleaders, and these had been stating their case too often with an eye on what the United States had to give in a material sense. So much had this been the case that many Americans had grown tired and suspicious, and small blame to them, too.

The project was discussed from all its angles. When I was asked my own considered viewpoint I said that I did not think I should go to America and get audiences simply to lecture them. If I went at all I should go as an artiste, doing my work as I had done for many years but always accepting any opportunity of putting the British case before the people of the States. Curiously enough at the very time the question of my going over the Atlantic was being discussed in high diplomatic quarters an urgent invitation arrived from my friends in New York. Here was a way out of any difficulty. I cabled back at once stating my willingness to go on condition that I was allowed a free hand to speak as much as I cared to, quite apart from my professional duties, on Britain's part in the titanic struggle. This was agreeable to my friends both in London and in New York and a few days later it was announced that the American Y. M. C. A. had invited me to make use of their great organization to address the youth of America.

So once more I found myself on the Atlantic. The U-boat menace was very real at this time and I remember we spent one or two most anxious days on board the *Mauretania*, especially when we were running without lights at night. I had been under shell-fire in France several times but it always seemed to me that there was something tangible, as it were, in land warfare—at least you had a chance of being missed or passed over! At sea, on the other hand, with invisible and swift Death hissing its way towards you from beneath the waves a full ship-load of innocent and helpless people might be launched into Eternity in a few moments. Bullets and shells, it appeared to me, were inhuman enough; torpedoes an invention of the Devil himself! I never was at ease while on board ship all through the war years. But though I crossed the Atlantic and the English channel many, many times between 1914 and 1918 I never saw an enemy submarine at close quarters.

I fired the first shot in my new American campaign at a great gathering in the Hippodrome, New York. It was held on a Sunday evening and the big building was crowded to the doors. The platform party embraced many notable and important figures in the civic and business life of the city. There was also a good sprinkling of well-known British men and women present. I rather forget now just the lines I followed in my speech—the longest one I had ever delivered in my life up till that night—but I told them all about my trip to the war zone and laid special emphasis on the work done at home by the women of Britain, France, and Belgium. My idea was to give American womanhood some idea of the responsibility that lay before them when their own men went to the war. All my life, at all events since I first started going to America, I have had a very genuine regard for the women of America. They are the most purposeful and completely competent women in all the world and well I realized how vital it was to have them heart and soul behind their husbands and sons in the field. Throughout my campaign I addressed myself particularly to the women. That opening night in New York they listened to me with rapt attention; I could perceive many wet eyes as the women followed my stories of feminine bravery and sacrifice across the sea. And how they laughed, too, at my tale of the Englishwoman scrubbing the floor of a Red Triangle hut at a base in France. "Hi, there!" she called out to a young soldier passing along the hut. "Bring me some more water, will you?" The young man stopped, looked down at the woman in astonishment and replied, "My good person, I'm an officer. Dash it all, you can't address an officer like that." Quick as lightning came the retort from the woman with the scrubbing-brush in her hand, "Dash it all, man, I'm a Duchess."

The significance of the story was fully appreciated. After the laughter had died down I pointed out that that was the spirit in which all our people, rich and poor, high and low, were conducting the war. And then, towards the close of my remarks, I warned the women of America that soon the long lists of casualties would be flashing to them beneath

Photo. by Anderson

SIR HARRY ADDRESSES FIFTEEN THOUSAND IN SAN FRANCISCO

the tides, spoke of the heart-pains and the tragedies that
were bound to come, and counselled them to clench their
teeth and hold fast to the purpose of victory. This New
York war rally in the Hippodrome was the grandest meeting I have ever addressed in my life. I shall never forget it.
The papers published full reports and I was inundated with
requests for speeches from all over the country. Before leaving New York I was invited to speak outside the Sub Treasury on the occasion of a big Victory Bond demonstration.
The chairman on that occasion was U. S. Vice-President
Marshall, if my memory serves me rightly, and we sold over
half a million dollars' worth of Bonds in a few minutes.
It was estimated that the crowd amounted to fully two hundred thousand people. The enthusiasm was so intense that
my emotion got the better of me and I cried for very joy
to think that this mighty nation was now with us in the
conflict. If at times I had begun to despair of the war being
soon over I now felt that complete victory could not long
be denied the Allies, supported and encouraged by the soul
and the endless resources of America. That great surging,
cheering, high-spirited concourse at Wall Street did me more
good than anything else for months. I was so affected that
I had to go home to my hotel and lie down for an hour or
two.

Of course every town I visited did not respond so readily
or so whole-heartedly as did the people of the vast commercial metropolis. Here and there my efforts were frowned
upon. I was again told that I was not wanted in my capacity
of British booster. Open hostility was shown to my work
in some places. Misunderstandings and criticisms met me
at many turns. Even newspapers which had been marvel-
lously kind to me as an artiste were severe in their condemna-
tions of my war speeches. Threats were levelled against me
in cities where the German element was strong. But I felt
like a soldier; I was "carrying on" for the sake of my coun-

try and my dead son. Occasionally I was encouraged in a very difficult task by incidents which proved to me that, after all, America was really with the Old Country in sentiment and ideals and in her determination to put a stop to the Bloody Thing. A poem which appeared about me in one of the New York weekly journals gave me much pleasure at the time. I came across it a few days ago when rummaging among my American documents and readers of my memoirs may forgive me if I reprint it here.

THE FIERY CROSS
(Dedicated to Harry Lauder)

He stood behind the footlights and he set the crowd a-laughing
With the same old crooning chuckle that we loved in other years,
And only those who knew could guess the grief behind the daffing
But for those who did, the laughter had a secret salt of tears.
Then at the last he came out in his grass-green coat and bonnet
With his gaudy tartans coloured like a garden in the sun,
The same quaint little figure—but a different face was on it
When he sang about the laddies that so well had fought and won.

A face lined hard with furrows where the plough of pain had driven.
Blue eyes that now were shadow-set through many a sleepless night,
The face of one who more than life ungrudgingly had given
Who called on us to do as well—and, ah! we owned his right.
We saw in him the Fiery Cross of Scotland, charred and gory
And our spirit burned within us to the challenge that he gave,
For the player was a prophet as he spoke his people's glory,
"We're a wee land, and a puir land, but, by God above, we're brave."

Please do not think for a moment that I take the liberty of reprinting these verses because I agree with their all too flattering picture of myself at the time of which I am writing. But they certainly represented the spirit in which I appeared before the American public in 1917. The authoress signed herself "Amelia J. Burr," but I do not know her and never met her. Many different people sent me copies of the *New York Outlook* in which the poem appeared and the mere fact that they did so showed that my efforts were being generally appreciated—and understood.

My theatre work was interspersed daily with attendances at Rotary and Kiwanis Club meetings, with trips to U. S. Training Camps, or cantonments as they were called, and with private functions all convened for the pursuit of war aims and movements. My Sundays were given up entirely to entertaining the troops in training. Here I would like to say a word or two concerning the magnificent young manhood which represented the first fruits of the United States war effort. These boys were simply wonderful. Every manjack of them was a study in physical and mental fitness. They filled me with intense admiration, reminding me of the early Scottish regiments that had marched away to battle three years before. And their spirit was as high as their bodies were clean and strong and handsome. With all the American soldiers I was a great favourite I am glad to say and they sang my choruses with lusty glee and vim. I wrote a song specially for "the boys" and taught them to sing it as well. It was entitled "Marching With the President." It was sung in every camp all over the States and also in France later on.

To see young America in training for the art and practice of war, as I saw her in these months of '17, was to realize something of the greatness of this robust, vital, energetic, and pulsating nation. Probably no American citizen, with the exception of several in high places, had half the opportunities I had of seeing the flower of her young army. Here were indeed Lindberghs in the making—many of them. Clear-eyed, clean-mouthed, frank of face, heads held high; I was as proud of them as though they had been wearing the tartans of my own land. And when they went to France they fought with tremendous gallantry as I knew they would. Never mind who won the war! If you really ask me that question I will tell you. I was asked it once at a big social affair in New York two or three years ago and the answer I made them is the answer I will give you now—"After long and serious consideration of the whole subject I have come to the conclusion that the English and the French and the

Belgians and the Americans all admirably assisted Scotland
to win the war!"

The National Security League was one of the most
important organizations in the States during the war. It
was my privilege frequently to co-operate with the League
in its mass meetings. It was a real "ginger" body and a
lady who had much to do with its success was Mrs. Preston
(formerly Mrs. Grover Cleveland) whose work as secretary
was tireless and indefatigable. She and I had many long
"cracks" together about the League and its labours. There
can be no doubt that the N. S. L. rendered service which
for precision and thoroughness can seldom have been
equalled in a national emergency. Altogether I found America, during the latter months of 1917, in a grip of war
fervour I had never thought, even dimly, possible. This
fervour conscripted industry, intellect, wealth, time and devo-
tion of men, women and children in a manner which amazed
me then and has amazed me ever since. Happy shall I always
be that I was able to lend a humble hand in this period in
the history of the country. Hail, Columbia!

This tour took me from coast to coast. I also spent several weeks in Canada, going right up to Montreal from
Boston. I was now, as you may imagine, worked up to a
white heat of enthusiasm and patriotism. I felt that it was
now or never. I knew the situation at home. I had just
come from the States where a wave of war effort, tremendous and unparalleled in its own way, was sweeping
everything before it. It had been arranged that I should
address the Montreal Rotarians immediately on my arrival.
I looked forward with immense delight to renewing my
intimate and enjoyable relations with my Canadian friends.
I had a lot to tell them, too, of the immortal bravery of their
own Canadian troops at the front—soldiers who had carved
their names in letters of Fire and Death while serving with
one or other of the British corps on the Somme, the Ancre,

or in Flanders. It was common knowledge in Europe that
the Canadians had proved amongst the very best and most
gallant fighters in all the dramatic happenings of the past
eighteen months. Britain was ringing with their exploits.
With all this on my mind I was distressed, on reaching
Montreal, to find so many young and splendid fellows strolling about the streets. I could not believe my eyes as I walked
down St. James' Street and observed crowds of what I
deemed to be eligible men in mufti.

Naturally, the first thing I did, on rising to my feet at
the Rotarian lunch, was to make reference to the impression
that was uppermost in my mind. I did not stop to think of
any racial or religious or political undercurrents among the
French Canadians. As a matter of honest fact I knew of
none. I am no politician, thank God, and I have always said
just what I thought at most times, thank God again. But
when I began to speak at that meeting about Mother France
pouring forth her dearest blood from every vein and asked
if the French blood in Canada was not mingling as freely as
it ought with that of the Motherland I sensed that I had
ventured on dangerous ground. My speech created a furore.
What I said was said in all innocence, with one desire only
in my heart—to strengthen the hands of those who were
fighting for the security and the sanctity of human rights.
But I was entirely misjudged. The Montreal newspapers did
not do anything to lessen the turmoil my speech had created;
one or two of them fanned the flames and openly accused
me of referring to the citizens of the town in terms of oppro-
brium and race prejudice. The excitement was terrific. By
tea-time the town was in a swirl of rage at Harry Lauder and
his insolent speech. Aggressive callers at the hotel and angry
ringers-up on the telephone showed how much I had an-
noyed certain citizens. I was casually threatened with bodily
punishment for my presumption. My friends advised me to
stay indoors for the rest of the night and some of them

implored me to cancel my week's show at the theatre. Both pieces of advice I refused to act upon. Instead I put on my kilt and Balmoral bonnet and walked alone as far as St. Catherine Street and St. Lawrence Boulevard. I was not molested in any way but I had to listen to many awkward and nasty observations. Guards were posted outside the place where I was living and I was told that troops were being held in readiness to cope with any outbreak that might take place. At eight o'clock I drove down to His Majesty's Theatre and had a great reception from a large crowd. The theatre itself was full to the doors and after my performance I made my usual speech but refrained from adding any fuel to the fire I had unwittingly kindled earlier in the day.

All this matter of the Montreal adventure I refer to now so that I can officially and emphatically deny that there was anything behind the remarks which caused such a sensation. As God is my witness I had not the slightest intention of coming across anybody's fingers or interfering with religious or political affairs or complications. I am getting to be an old man now and as my record and reputation are everything to me I wish them to bear no stain of prejudice or unworthy motive, particularly in the work I attempted to do during the Great War.

From Montreal to Toronto. Any fear that I might have forfeited the affection of my Canadian admirers was dispelled for ever from my mind by the extraordinary reception I received there. And in every other city in Canada throughout that tour the same story was told—"We are with the dear Old Mother Country to the last man and the last dollar!"

CHAPTER NINETEEN

MY FRIENDS THE PRESIDENTS

As I have told you somewhere within the last few paragraphs I had a long talk with President Woodrow Wilson during my '17 tour. He and Mrs. Wilson had attended the theatre in Washington when I was playing there and the two of them had joined enthusiastically in singing the chorus of my song "Marching With the President." It was arranged that I should go and have tea with them at the White House before my tour ended. This I was very pleased to do. As a matter of fact I have been a pretty constant visitor to the White House for twenty years. I have met all the Presidents during that period and have had unique opportunities for forming first-hand impressions of the illustrious American statesmen who have ruled the destinies of the States from Theodore Roosevelt down to the present occupant of the presidential chair. With more than one of these remarkable men I am proud to say I have been on terms of friendship. It may not be considered presumptious on my part, therefore, if I attempt a few very brief pen-pictures of the various Presidents whom it has been my privilege and honour to meet. I offer them in all humility and sincerity.

At the moment I have been referring to Woodrow Wilson. For this extraordinarily gifted man I conceived an almost perfervid admiration after the publication of his world-message marking the entry of the United States into the war. Like all Scotsmen I react very quickly either to oratory on the platform or eloquence in the written word. And I still remember the thrill which went through my being on reading this noble example of brilliant prose composition, backed as it was by lofty ideals and full of the most sublime

moral thoughts. I almost worshipped President Wilson as
a result of that, to me, immortal Note. If, perhaps, I had reason in after years slightly to alter my opinion of President
Wilson's claim to world greatness let me say at once that I
still regard him as an amazingly able man who just missed
the chances given him of achieving deathless fame. I write
as I feel. I am no master of the art of literary analysis; this
requires gifts which I do not possess and learning which
I have never acquired. But I do think my many and constant
years of travel have enabled me to form rather shrewd, even
if casual, judgments of the really prominent people with
whom I have been brought in contact.

Woodrow Wilson looked to me exactly what he was—a
schoolmaster. That long, clean-shaven face, the cold logic in
his eyes, the lines about his mouth, in fact every outward
aspect of the man savoured of the university class-room.
If you had put on his head a mortar-cap, underneath his
arm a couple of books, and in his right hand a cane you
would have got the perfect dominie. I am told that few
people ever warmed to him. He certainly over-awed me
when I met him. When he shook hands with me I thought
he did it coldly and perfunctorily but he allowed a beam of
genuine enthusiasm to creep into his eyes as he thanked me
for what I had done in the way of entertaining the American
troops. While he spoke I thought what a remarkably well-
groomed man he was. He was as neat and "kenspeckle"
(Scots for dainty) as a new pin. He appeared to me to
have devoted a good deal of attention to his personal adornment before leaving his bedroom that morning.

We are too close to him to estimate Mr. Wilson's real
worth either as an American or as a world statesman. It may
be that he will only properly be appraised many years hence.
Be that as it may it seems to me that we can attribute to
him some work that must live, some dreams of his that may
come true. Should the League of Nations ever grow strong—

as I, for one, sincerely hope it will—and become what Wilson thought it might, he will go down into history as the Father of the League. He will be remembered as a coiner of great phrases, many of them electrifying as they were beautiful. He will be remembered as one of the most aloof, stern, stubborn men that ever occupied the White House, yet the possessor of one of the greatest brains America has produced. He will be remembered as the President who went abroad, animated by high principles and with only good in his heart, and came a sad purler when he pitted his abilities against the astuteness and the finesse of men like Clemenceau and David Lloyd George and other politicians trained in the wiles and subtleties of European intrigue. I often wish that Woodrow Wilson had stayed in America at the end of the war. Many and many a time when I am ruminating on my wandering career and the famous men I have met my mind goes back to Woodrow Wilson and somehow or other I heave a sigh. I still think he was a very, very great man. And I know hundreds of Americans who think as I do.

What a difference between Wilson and Theodore Roosevelt! I had the joy of meeting "Teddy" more than once during his Presidency. He looked for all the world what you would expect a man to look who wielded the "Big Stick" with crushing effect against all comers, whether these opponents chanced to be Spaniards in the block-houses of San Juan Hill, an untameable broncho 'way out West, a lion in the African jungle, poisonous snakes in the fever-infested swamps along the River of Doubt—or a political opponent anywhere. Roosevelt would clench his fist (this was my very first impression of him) and penetrate with his keen eye until there was left no glimmer of doubt as to the man's intense earnestness and his fixed purpose to see right through whatever job he undertook. His massive shoulders, his prominent teeth, the half squint in his eye, his rather unkempt moustache, all contributed to make him a formidable personality. But often there came into his face the light of full enjoyment of a humorous remark or situation. He could laugh as heartily as he fought doggedly. And whenever I shook hands with him I decided that here was a man of broad and kindly humanity. I loved him from the outset.

Roosevelt was a magnificent figure in American life for many years. I read in a London newspaper the other day that a very eminent German biographer, Emil Ludwig, had made the pointed statement that "Bismarck and Roosevelt are the two outstanding figures of the past hundred years." I do not propose to examine this observation in any way and only quote it to show how powerfully the redoubtable Teddy impressed himself upon the world. Surely he was the most many-sided President America has ever had. When I first went to the States I simply could not understand why he was either madly loved or violently hated. It was a complete enigma to me until I began to realize some of the forces the bull-dog President was up against. His enemies openly cursed and slandered him. I was tremendously interested (and as keenly shocked) to come across some printed villifications of the President the like of which we would never have tolerated in the press of Britain. I cut out some of these published tirades at the time and put them away beside my American "souvenirs" from among which I have just retrieved them. They struck me then as being so terrible, applied to the President of the country, and yet so picturesque in phraseology that I decided to keep them as curios. One political opponent referred to him as "this roaring, ring-tailed, buck-jumping prophet," while the other applied the tar and feathers in this language—"Had the President been dammed by Sycorax (who this lady was I haven't the foggiest idea but she can't have been nice to know), sired by the Devil, and born in Hell he would disgrace his parents and dishonour his country no more!" Of course I don't know what Teddy had said about the fellows who made these delicate come-backs at him; probably he had stirred 'em up considerable!

Roosevelt told me once that the one word he hated most was "Can't." He taught his sons to hate it too. When they were wee lads their father used to construct what seemed the most impassable obstacles and tell them they must get through. They generally did get through and the result is that these sons today are truly of the lion's brood. Teddy hit hard but he hit square. I am doubtless partial in all that I have said about him because I liked him so much, but I am convinced that his old enemies will today concede that "the elements were so mixed in him that Nature might stand up and say to all the world—this was a man!"

When I first met Big Bill Taft I thought he was the finest tonic against the blues in all broad America. We had a great game of golf together at Augusta, Georgia, and I took the liberty of beating the President by two holes. We must have cut a pretty comic figure on the links together, he with his tremendous bulk and me with my small stature. He may have improved his golf game since these days but when we had our famous match he was most erratic. If he connected with the ball he swiped it a long distance but my recollection is that oftener than not he shifted a large part of the links without propelling the pill very far. But he smiled all the time; in fact I don't think I have ever met a man with so dominating a smile. He simply exuded geniality. As Chief Justice of the Supreme Court he may have settled down to a more sombre bearing and in that case I shall not visit him while he is on duty "on the bench" because I would not like my memories of him to be other than those of a great big fat laughing boy making the best of everything in this best of possible worlds.

A special friend of mine in London knew "Bill" well when he was Governor General of the Philippine Islands after the Spanish American war. He assures me that without doubt Mr. Taft was the most unpopular man in the islands among his own people but the most popular with the Philippinos—whom he persisted in calling his "Little Brown Brothers." At that time the Americans in the islands had not much use for the natives on account of certain little traits in their character—since, I am told, happily eradicated—and a song which the former were wont to sing lustily in Manila finished up with these two lines—

> They may be brothers of William H. Taft
> But they ain't no kin to me!

Well, I can't imagine Big Bill being anything else to anybody—with the exception, perhaps, of those whom he has to decide against in his official capacity as judge—but a jolly big brother. Here is a story about the ex-president which I am assured is true and if it's not true it ought to be. It made me smile when I heard it from one of Bill's own old friends. Away back in the early nineties Mr. Roosevelt sent Taft to Rome to confer with the existing Pope regarding some important religious question affecting the Philippine Islands. He was invited to attend some big function at St. Peter's Cathedral and, to his dismay, found upon arrival that everybody was in evening dress—a strict rule observed for certain Roman ceremonies even at high noon. The American envoy was politely told that he could not enter unless he was suitably attired in orthodox fashion. Mr. Taft realized that he would not have time to go to his hotel and change so he walked into the street and rolled heavily into the nearest restaurant with the idea of borrowing a dress suit from one of the waiters. Finding a waiter of anything like Bill's majestic proportions must have seemed rather a forlorn hope. But the gods of chance were this day stoutly backing the stout one. There *was* a monstrous waiter in the restaurant. Out came a fat "wad" and a deal was made on the spot. The waiter and the future President retired for a

few minutes and before the function at St. Peter's had
progressed very far Mr. Taft arrived back and was duly
"passed in." The fact that the sleeves were a few inches
too short, that the waistcoat showed signs here and there
of "ministroné," and that a serious and imminent strain was
put on the buttons of the commandeered trousers mattered
not one little bit to the genial William Howard; he had
been faced with a sudden problem and had overcome it with
as sudden action. I would like to see "Bill" in one of my
kilts!

The late Warren G. Harding was one of the most handsome Americans it has been my pleasure to meet. I had
breakfast with him on one occasion at the White House.
The reception he gave me was cordial in the extreme. We
spoke about many things over our eggs and bacon but princi-
pally about the war and the condition in which it would leave
Europe for many, many years to come. Mr. Harding was a
homely man and a rare good booster for his native Ohio.
When I told him that I knew Ohio very well, including his
own town of Marion, he was as pleased as Punch, to quote
an English phrase, and, looking across the table he remarked,
"Say, Harry, ain't Marion just one swell little town?" I
agreed and added that it would now be much more famous
since his elevation to the Presidency. After breakfast we
motored out to the Congressional Golf Course and the President and I played two other fellows, one of whom was Mr.
Eddie McLean the proprietor of the Washington Post. We
licked them by three up and two to go. On the course Mr.
Harding was like a schoolboy and he was, to use his own
words, just "tickled to death" by the good form we displayed. Our caddies were overjoyed at the success of our
side because I think they had a gamble on with the other
pair. At the finish I asked my boy what he had won and
he told me two dollars. "Then," said I, "you should hand
over a buck to me for I won most of the holes!" I suppose

this story is told against me at the Congressional Course to this day.

Warren Harding did not impress me as being in any way of the calibre of Roosevelt or Wilson. He was a plain honest man and was pleased to be known as such. The biggest thing he did, in my opinion, during his term was to deliver that very fine speech at the Washington Peace Conference. It sank deep into the hearts of the delegates from all over the world and made easier the solutions of the intricate problems dealt with by the Conference. I was sorry indeed to learn of the President's untimely end through pneumonia.

Calvin Coolidge I met first when he was Governor of Massachusetts. It was either before or after the famous Police Strike—I forget now—but I was immensely interested in the man who gave this dictum to the United States and to the world—"There is no right to strike against the public safety of anybody, anywhere, anytime." This remark, I have often since been told, had more to do than anything else with his being made Vice-President as the nominee of the Republican Party. The death of President Harding gave "Cal" his chance and in my opinion he not only accepted it with both hands but stepped right into the foreground of Great Presidents.

Accident may have made him first citizen at the time but ability has kept him there. I met him again soon after he took office and he gave me a very pleasant hour or two at the White House. Calvin Coolidge looks precisely as he ought to. He is a close-mouthed, close-fisted Yankee from Granite Lands and his personal appearance bears it out. He can speak all right when he feels inclined to; of that fact Lady Lauder and I had ample and charming proof. But there is no denying that the tight lines of his mouth give him an aspect of stony silence—almost of deep mystery. You can never tell what Mr. Coolidge is thinking. But my impression of him is that no matter what he is thinking

SIR HARRY AND LADY LAUDER WITH PRESIDENT CALVIN COOLIDGE AT THE WHITE HOUSE

he is always thinking right. If I wrote—or tried to write—a column about America's present President I am certain that I couldn't improve upon the last sentence!

I heard a very good story about "Cal" just as I was leaving New York a few months ago. It may have been published before but it is worth repeating. A visitor to the White House with whom the Coolidges were on friendly terms took the liberty of a little jest with Mrs. Coolidge in her husband's presence. "Say, Mrs. Coolidge," remarked the visitor, "you look talked to death!" The President did not wait for his wife to reply but suddenly flashed out "Mr.——, I have always noticed that the remarks I don't make cause me the least trouble!" Wasn't that a "beaut"?

Another yarn I like about the President runs as follows: Some time ago he gave a palpable propagandist an interview. This guy was a very fine talker, the sort that could sway big audiences off their feet and set them cheering. With Mr. Coolidge he put forth his best and most convincing efforts in the way of facts and phrasing. He felt sure that he was making good. When he had finished and was all alert to note the effect of his oratory the President pointed to one of the White House pussycats which was in the room and remarked, "See that cat? She has walked round the table three times since you began talking!" And that was all. The interview ended.

I like stories about men like Calvin Coolidge and here is another one which may be new to many people. During an official visit to the White House a certain gentleman said to the President that he would greatly appreciate the gift of a cigar from the President, not for himself but for a friend who had the eccentricity of collecting cigar-bands from famous smokers all over the world. The President thought the matter out for a few seconds, then rose and stepped over to a table on which rested a box of cigars. Taking one out he carefully removed the band, replaced the cigar in the box and handed the band to his visitor. Economy raised to the *nth* degree! Speaking about cigars (and economy!) reminds me of a story they tell in Glasgow against myself. The tale goes that I once got a box of cigars presented to me by an admirer, that I thanked him very much for his kindness and casually asked the name of the shop-keeper from whom he had purchased them thus enabling me to slip down next morning and exchange the cigars for a pound or two of thick black!

In spite of all that they say about "Silent Cal" and the difficulty of getting him to open his mouth I have the idea that a notable change is coming over him. If I were asked to explain what I mean I would say that success is going to his heart and not to his head. The hard lines about his mouth seem to be getting a wee bit softer. The sorrow of losing a son and a father are, after all, taking some of the coldness from that inscrutable face and putting a look of concern, even tenderness, into his eyes. For Mr. Coolidge has a fine soul. There is something great and there is something noble in a man who, immediately he is sworn in as President of the United States in an old Vermont farmhouse, does not dash on to Washington accompanied by a swarm of newspaper men, but walks out alone in the grey dawn to his mother's grave. I think I know what prayers he said there; what guidance he implored from God and from his mother.

I am afraid I have rather digressed from the purely personal side of my memoirs to indulge in these humble reflections on the American Presidents whom it has been my privilege to meet. Next to the Prime Minister of my own country I have always regarded the ruling President of the United States as by far the most important personage in world politics and influence. His powers for good or evil are incalculable and it says much for the inherent common-sense of the people of the United States that they have selected so many brilliant figures to adorn their Presidential Chair and add lustre to the history of their nation. If I were an American father I would, as a solemn duty, insist on my children reading the life story of every President from Washington downwards. Perhaps, of course, every child in the States does so today—but I "hae ma doots."

CHAPTER TWENTY

GLEN BRANTER

BRITISH readers of my Memoirs may be inclined to complain that I have dealt at too great length with my American experiences and impressions. But they must not forget that quite a large proportion of my life has been spent in the United States and in the British Dominions overseas. I have indeed been a persistent wanderer for more than twenty years and it is difficult for me to tell anything like a comprehensive story of my life without these frequent wanderings into other lands and among other people. Besides, my "home supporters" should remember also that there were always very substantial inducements of a financial nature dangling at the end of every other voyage across the foam. I could have remained and worked the British halls for nine or ten months in each year, earning enough to keep the wolf from the door. But I found that the oftener I went away for an extended period the greater was my welcome back in London and the Provinces. In London alone I used to play seasons of six or eight weeks in one theatre and all old professionals will tell you that this is a most comfortable and pleasant way of working—if you are sufficiently popular to fill the house at every performance.

For another thing the joy of getting home again after a long and arduous foreign tour has always been very real, so far as I am concerned. The last day or two on the steamship ploughing her way nearer and nearer Southampton or Liverpool have invariably seen me in a highly excited condition as in fancy I once again trod the heather hills of Argyllshire or strolled through the West-end of dear old London. Yes, even such a trick as Blackwood played on me

recently at Waterloo Station could not damp the wild enthusiasm with which I always return to my own country.
The incident I mention took place just outside the station.
There was a whole bunch of camera men wanting to snap
me but for some curious reason they saved their "ammuni-
tion" until we got near a cab-rank. The boys posed me right
up against the front of a taxi and asked me to smile my
broadest smile at the same time pointing with one finger in
the direction of a placard stuck on the front window of the
cab. I did as I was told never troubling to read the placard
and it was not until next morning that I discovered the real
significance of the photograph prominently displayed in
every London newspaper. There was Harry Lauder standing beside a taxi-cab and gleefully pointing to a notice "Great
Reduction in Fares." In response to a request for something
special from the press photographers the jocular Blackwood
had hit upon this amusing idea, well knowing that it would
go down with the public as a "characteristic Lauder touch!"

I had fairly long spells at home both in 1917 and '18.
There were many contracts waiting to be worked off in different towns all over the country but I did manage to get
an occasional spell at Dunoon or Glen Branter. Up till the
time of John's death his mother and I were exceedingly
fond of our Highland estate. It was a wild but a bonnie
place. I had farms and moorland and hills, with fine stretches
of fishing in the rivers and on Loch Eck. The house itself
was large and comfortable, with every possible modern con-
venience, and Invernoaden, close by, had been put into
thorough repair against the time when John and his bride
would come home to it. John's death at the front knocked
all our schemes and our dreams on the head. The Glen
became tenanted with ghosts. At every turn we were
reminded of our dear lad; what might have been was ever
uppermost in our thoughts. One spot we fondly loved in
spite of the shattering of all our hopes. It was a beautiful

knoll on the north side of the main road from Dunoon to Strachur. From its summit we could look right across the glen to the two houses, and the vista, no matter whether the sun smiled or the Highland mist was hanging low over the hills, always made a strong appeal to my wife and I. Here, we resolved, would be set up a monument to John's memory. And in due time a simple but striking redstone monolith crowned the top of the grassy knoll. Inside the iron railings surrounding John's memorial we left sufficient room for a grave on either side—one for Nance and the other for myself.[1]

Frankly, I do not think that I was ever fated to settle down as a Highland "laird." Certainly I was never meant to be a farmer; of that I am now convinced. But conviction only came after my experiences had cost me a tremendous amount of money. To begin with I bought Glen Branter on the "top of the market" for properties of this description. It was so far from civilization (I merely use the phrase in its popular sense for, make no mistake, the people of our Highland glens are among God's elect not only for kindliness of heart but in character and intellectual equipment) that building, alterations and improvements generally were on a very costly scale. Moreover my luck as an agriculturist always seemed to be dead out. If I bought five thousand sheep at four pounds a head, hoping they would soon be worth five with a general food shortage prevalent all over Great Britain, I was to discover a few weeks later that the price had gone down instead of rising. If I purchased another two thousand at three pounds a head to "level up" the next advice I had from my manager was that sheep values had dropped to "ten bob a leg." If I planted ten thousand young trees in the faith and hope that some day they would grow into valuable timber, or at least lend

[1] (Lady Lauder is buried on the right-hand side of the monument to the memory of her son.)

a picturesque aspect to an otherwise uninteresting piece of
land, the ravenous deer came down from the hills overnight
and devoured every shoot! If I built a dam across a stream
to make a reservoir "the rain descended and the floods came"
sweeping away the labour of months. If I paid a hundred
and twenty pounds each for a pair of Clydesdales I found
they were only worth half the money a month or two later.
Again, if I reared a pedigree foal of considerable potential
value it was sure to fall and break a leg; if I acquired half
a dozen aristocratic milch cows at an aristocratic price four
of them—at least!—were almost certain to die of some
mysterious disease never before known in that part of Scotland. And if I set out, as I did, to build a few new roads
through the estate I very speedily discovered that it would
have been cheaper to construct a couple of residential thor-
oughfares through the busiest parts of London!

All my life, right up to the time I became one myself,
I had envied the "landed gentleman" with his life of freedom in the open-air, his horses, his cattle, his dogs, his
fruitful fields—everything "yielding its increase" even while
he slept. Don't you believe a word of it. The picture is all
wrong. I know. I've had some. I was lucky to get out of
Glen Branter with my leather leggings and a haunch of
preserved venison! Fortunately the Forestry Commission of
the British Government came along with an offer soon after
the war to take over the Glen for afforestation purposes.
With bankruptcy staring me in the face, or at least, shall I
say, peering its ugly head round the corner, I accepted the
offer. My farming and stock-breeding ambitions were dead.
I might be a good enough comedian, I told myself, but I
had proved a rank failure as a prosperous country squire!

Joking apart, however, we would never have left the
Glen had John lived. It is situated in one of the loveliest
parts of Argyllshire, a county which I adore beyond all
others in Scotland. It grows the finest larch trees and flower-

ing shrubs in Great Britain. Its sweeping hills are populated by the blue hare, the fox, the raven, the black-cock and the buzzard-hawk. "Bunny" roams and multiplies everywhere in spite of the presence of its natural enemy, the "whutterit," to employ our old Scots word for the weasel and stoat. I still have my home in Dunoon, and when my time arrives to pass over I shall go to rest beside John's monument on the top of the little hill "up the Glen."

CHAPTER TWENTY-ONE

KNIGHT OF THE BRITISH EMPIRE

FROM 1918 until this year (I am writing in the early summer months of 1927) I have been consumed with a restlessness which has kept far in the background all thoughts of settling down to the quieter life I had been looking forward to before and during the war. The loss of John completely altered the course of his mother's life and mine. As I have told you we were glad to give up Glen Branter and Laudervale was now our only retreat, for we never established a really permanent home in London. But here again there were too many sad memories for us to feel happy for more than a few days at a time. Travel and work were the only things that could take our minds off our sorrow. So during these nine years we did a tremendous amount of globe-trotting.

A day or two after the Armistice in November, 1918, we found ourselves on the old *Mauretania,* the first liner to leave England for America after the declaration of peace. There were over five thousand United States troops on board with a mere handful of ordinary passengers. Lady Lauder and Mrs. Vallance, Tom's wife, were the only women making the trip—an almost unique experience in Atlantic travel. Talk about floating hotels! On that run the *Mauretania* was turned into a series of gigantic military mess-rooms: there were meals being served from early morning until late at night. When the ship got into New York, where she and her soldier passengers had an amazingly enthusiastic reception, the stewards and orderlies must have been fit to fall asleep on their feet. I calculated that something just under a hundred thousand meals must have been served on board during the five days' sail. The *Mauretania* was heavy with food

233

when we left England; when we arrived in the Hudson she was sticking clear up out of the water!

It was most interesting to me to talk to the returning U. S. dough-boys. They were a grand lot of chaps and full of stories about the war, and their experience in it. Many of them who had been brigaded for service with British units early in the days of America's entry into the struggle entertained me for hours with their vivid and picturesque impressions. Some of them had actually met friends of mine at the front and others who had heard me sing in different parts of the States had gone and visited John's grave on the Albert Road. I formed several friendships on that memorable trip across the Atlantic which I hope to retain for the rest of my life. There is a subtle bond in those war-time friendships which makes a special appeal to all of us, don't you think?

I have no intention of wearying my readers by categorical descriptions of my wanderings throughout the world during the past eight or nine years, but I feel that I would be "scamping" several of the most interesting and eventful years of my life if I did not refer, however briefly, to some of the incidents which stand out prominently in my later career and to some of the extraordinary men and women it has been my good fortune (or otherwise!) to come across in different parts of the world. Another thing that occurs to me is that many people everywhere may be expecting me to say something about the material rewards that have come to a public entertainer like myself who has achieved some measure of international popularity. Well, I *may* feel inclined, before I have finished, to let you into my confidence—partially, at least!—on this highly delicate personal point, but all I will admit in the meantime is that the Income Tax authorities of the wide world seem to have done themselves very proudly out of Harry Lauder. Had these persistent and insistent fellows been non-existent it is just possible that I might have scraped enough to live on quietly long before this time of day!

We went over again to Australia from 'Frisco at the end of my 1918-19 American tour. My party arrived in Sydney on the first of March to experience a repetition of the boisterous welcome scenes which had marked my first visit in '14. Seated at lunch in the Hotel Australia on the day of our arrival a telegram was handed to Tom Vallance. He opened it. I was speaking to John Tait and Ted Carroll at the time and paid no attention. Tom got up from his chair, came round the table to where I was seated and held out his hand. "Congratulations, Sir Harry!" was all he said. Turning to his sister, my wife, he said "Nance, you're now Lady Lauder!" We were all tremendously excited and we eagerly read the cable again and again. It contained the brief statement that His Majesty the King had been graciously pleased to confer on me a Knighthood of the British Empire. Bye and bye Nance and Mrs. Vallance started to cry, so between tears and general congratulations all round we had a very happy luncheon party.

Later in the day cables began to roll in from home, from America and elsewhere—hundreds of them—all containing congratulations. In the first flush of my pleasure and enthusiasm I determined to reply to them all individually, also by cable, but when Tom (wise fellow!) submitted an estimate of the cost I abandoned the idea and just wrote letters of thanks. This job, I remember, occupied all my spare time for a fortnight.

I made my first public appearance as a Knight of the British Empire at Sydney on the night of Easter Saturday, 1919. The newspapers, of course, had had the information as soon as I had and they printed the news, together with long appreciations of myself, under suitably big headlines. The result was that I got a magnificent reception from a crowded audience when I stepped from the wings. The people rose and cheered me again and again. As I stood there waiting for the tumult to die down my thoughts were of a very mixed character. To tell the truth I was nearer bursting into tears than swelling with pride at the distinguished honour my King has seen fit to confer on me. A man's mind works very quickly on such occasions. During the minute or two I stood on the stage at Sydney that evening before starting to sing "I Love a Lassie," my whole life passed in flashing snap-shots before my mental vision. My poverty-stricken early days, the hard, sweating toil in the mines of Lanarkshire, the struggles and the strivings and the ambitions to make good on the concert platform, the gradual crescendo of success as a theatre celebrity, my world tours and the laughter and cheers of a million of people in two hemispheres, the fortune which I had honestly built up by my own unaided efforts—and now this great and unexpected honour as the culminating point in a colourful career! All these pictures, all these thoughts, came rapidly but clearly as I stood under the spotlights at Sydney that night. And I would willingly, aye, with great joy, have bartered the lot for one smile from John, one shake of his hand, to hear him say, "Dad, old man!" once more.

Altogether I have made four tours in Australia, including one in Tasmania, and three in New Zealand. For both of these magnificent island countries in the southern seas I have an immense admiration and a great love. Although comparatively close to each other—a matter of twelve hundred miles means nothing in the huge spaces of the South Pacific—they are entirely different in geographical characteristics and in the types of their peoples. New Zealand, as I think I have already said, is practically another Scotland and, seeing that this is so, it made an instantaneous appeal to my affections from the very outset. Its MacDonalds and MacIntoshes and MacLeans, with their Caledonian Societies and Burns Clubs and Gaelic Associations transform many of its towns and

ON THE *S.S. SONOMA*

SIR HARRY HAS A "COOLER" ON THE DECK BATH OF THE *S.S. SONOMA* IN THE SOUTH
PACIFIC

villages into purely Scottish "territory"; there are, I am
assured, thousands of Gaelic speakers in New Zealand who
have never seen, and never will see, the land they venerate
second only to their own. Scottish weekly and daily papers
are delivered in New Zealand in their tens of thousands. I
know one old man in Auckland who has had an Aberdeen
daily paper posted to him every day for thirty years. Immediately he gets his copy he scores out the dates from the tops
of the pages and writes in the day of the week on which it
arrives. Thus is Scottish sentiment and the news of Scotland
kept alive and warm ten or twelve thousand miles from
"home!" What Scot can help developing an extraordinary
affection for such a country and such a people?

I would like to sit down some day and start writing a
book about Australia. I might start—but I would never finish. The subject would be beyond me entirely. If a hundred
new books were to be written about Australia in the next
ten years their authors would only be able to touch the fringe
of the romance of this amazing island continent almost as
large as the United States of America but still with a population less than that of Greater London! Every time I return to
Australia I am filled with genuine enthusiasm for its fine,
healthy, hospitable people, its delightful climate, its magnificent harbours and cities, its present prosperity and its
unbounded possibilities for the future. I feel convinced that
Australia, within a reasonable period of time, is destined to
be one of the very greatest countries in the world. It is still
suffering from "growing pains" and has problems, difficult
and dangerous, yet to solve but it holds out opportunities and
a welcoming hand, to men and women who are willing to
work, such as cannot be found in any other part of the globe,
not even excepting the United States. If today, I were a
young man eager to push my fortunes in a new country I
think I would certainly go to Australia.

Many, many happy months have I spent out there and

many more do I hope to spend. There is hardly a town of any
size at all in Victoria, New South Wales, Queensland, or
Western Australia that I have not visited and played in; I
have crossed the continent from Brisbane to Perth by rail
more than once—an experience which long-distance travellers
in America ought to undergo if they want to know what a
week in a train can really be like. I have lived in sheep sta-
tions a hundred miles from a village, fished for strange fish
in streams and rivers never before whipped by rod and line,
wandered through vineyards and orange-groves heavily laden
with fruit which only California can match, watched the
pearl-fishers at Thursday Island, gone down the gold-mines
at Mount Morgan and Calgoorlie, and have been photographed alongside Aboriginal Chiefs in the Great Desert.
Yes, I think my knowledge of Australia is fairly first-hand
and when I say that of all the countries I know she has the
most glorious future I hope my readers will not imagine I
am giving my friends "down under" the usual traveller's
boost. We in Britain do not appreciate Australia as we ought
to; there should be stronger commercial ties between the
Commonwealth and the Old Mother Land. That these may
be developed and expanded for the benefit of both is my
sincere hope.

It has been my happy fortune to meet many of the most
eminent sons of Australia during my tours. I have lively
recollections of numerous talks with Mr. Hughes and Mr.
Bruce during their terms as Prime Minister. The statesmen
of the world have nothing on these alert, brilliant men both
of whom have visited Britain and impressed their personalities and intellects on the rulers and the people of the old
country. For the present Premier, Mr. Bruce, I have a particularly high esteem. He is a great man in every sense of the
word and Australia is proud of him. He and I had a round
of golf at Melbourne a year or two ago. He gave me an
unholy whacking but I was off my game that day. I am burn-

ing for my revenge, Mr. Prime Minister, and the next time we meet I'll take a third and even go the length of playing you for a golf-ball—the newest one I have in my bag!

Andrew Fisher is another splendid Australian patriot with whose friendship I have been honoured for several years now. So long as the island-continent continues to breed men of the stamp of Hughes and Bruce and Fisher, to say nothing of many fine-spirited and able State leaders and politicians, so long will there be a real and a ringing significance in the national motto—"Advance Australia!"

I wish I had room in these present memoirs to say all I would like to say about my adventures and experiences in different parts of Australia. But they are too long already and I feel I must guard myself against doing on the printed page what I have never (I hope) done on the stage—and that is bore my audience. Yet I feel strongly that any reference to Australia, short or long, which did not include some words about the Tait Brothers, and about Old John Brown of Newcastle, New South Wales, would be incomplete indeed.

The Tait brothers—there are five of them, Charles, John, Nevin, Edward and Frank—form an almost unique family combination. I have never met quite their equal anywhere in the world; certainly I have encountered no such wonderful brothers south of the line. They are natives of Victoria and were born in a small country town but their parents removed to Melbourne when the "loons" were very young. Charles, the eldest, joined the firm of Allan and Co., music publishers and concert agents and promoters. He managed to get employment for his brothers at these concerts in the capacity of check-takers, ushers, and general utility boys and, all of them being more than threatened with intelligence, they picked up an inkling of the business which was to stand them in good stead in after years. Their first big hit as impresarios was to bring Dame Clara Butt to Australia and, after her, the famous Besses o' the Barn Brass Band, winners of many Crystal Palace competitions taken part in by the best of the British bands—and don't forget that we have the finest brass bands in the world!

I was one of their next "successes" and while all my foreign tours have been controlled by my friend Ted Carroll I ought to explain that Mr. Carroll and the Taits have always worked hand-in-hand so far as my business in Australia and New Zealand is concerned. For all of the brothers I have a high regard but I am rather a difficult chap to control when I am working so it was early arranged between us that Ted would come in and take full charge of me. This happened thirteen years ago and the amicableness of the arrangement has been demonstrated by its results. You see, I can occasionally go off the deep end with one man but not with five. And if that one man has a grievance against me he is much more likely to make me see reason than five men would! At all events the Taits and I are on the most friendly terms. They have now business interests in all parts of Australia, having linked up some years ago with the famous firm of J. C. Williamson, Limited, and my own impression of these remarkable brothers is that they must by this time all have enough to get bread and cheese for the rest of their lives. The only one I ever had any trouble with was Charlie! We had gone into the waiting-room at Albury, where the trains of two different states meet and can't go any further because of the different gauges, and were ordering a slight refreshment when Charlie came up and offered to pay. "No, no," said I with my usual generous impulse. "We'll toss for it. Heads I win; tails you lose!" "Right," said Mr. Tait. Naturally he lost—and paid up like a man. But in the next train his mind started to ruminate on the terms of the toss. So he came to me in a very truculent spirit and cordial relationships were only restored by my agreeing to pay for the dinner at the next stopping place. Nevin Tait works exclusively in London and he it is now who books the vaudeville

and operatic stars who go out to the Antipodes, there to have
a splendid holiday and, in most cases, to pick up substantial
rewards in real money.

Of dear old John Brown I would like to write a great
deal. He is my first-night mascot all over Australia. Formerly
there were two of them, Brown and John Norton, the journalist genius and magnate who founded the Truth chain of
newspapers throughout the Commonwealth and whose proud
boast, up till the time he died, was that he had attended every
night of Harry Lauder's first tour, involving journeys of
many thousands of miles. Only John Brown is left now and
although he is getting on in years I hope he will live long
enough to accompany me on my final farewell tour of his
wonderful country. I am very fond of John. I know there
are many people in Australia who are not so fond of him!
For one thing he owns all the best race-horses and during his
lifetime he has won more than his just proportion of the
principal races. For another thing he is not—how shall I
put it?—exactly the most popular employer in the country on
account of a dour, stubborn, silent way he has of dealing
with strikes and labour effervescences generally. John would
rather shut up his coal mines in Newcastle, N.S.W., for a
twelvemonth than submit to conditions laid down by any
labour leader, or "soviet" committee, and he has what some
folks might think a nasty habit of "saying his say" in language forcible and to the point. Again, John does not speak
much about what he is going to do, either in business, on the
turf, or in the poultry show-ring. He just does it. For
instance, a year or two ago he astounded the poultry specialists of Australia by sweeping the boards at the Sydney
Easter Show. Such noble birds had never before been seen
anywhere "down under." They left all the other competitors
in a side street; reduced them wholesale to the "also-ran"
division! Where the devil did they come from? How on
earth did the old man manage to breed such an overpowering

collection of prize-winning certainties? They were the sensation of the Easter Show. John Brown had "done it on them again." Meantime Master Brown smiled his enigmatical smile and said nothing. He didn't feel at all called upon to tell either his friends or his enemies that he had imported every proud cock, every hen and chicken, from the pens of Lord Dewar in England, the mightiest poultry genius in the world today!

They tell me that John is the richest man in Australia. He may be. But all I know is that beneath his apparently hard exterior is a warm and kindly heart. He adored his aged mother to whom I often used to sing the "auld Scots sangs" when I went to visit them at their country estate outside Newcastle. She and her husband hailed from Lanarkshire. Last year I met old John—or young John, if you like it better—in London and he was just back from a visit to the scenes of his parents' childhood. There cannot, I always say, be much fundamentally wrong with a man who honours the memory of his father and his mother. John Brown does this—and I pay no attention at all to what some jaundiced folks say about him!

I have always made the return journey to Britain from Australia by way of the United States. To me it seems the natural route "back to the bens and the glens of home." For one thing I never get tired of the trip across the Pacific, with its calls at lovely Samoa or equally lovely Honolulu, and for another I have always known that Will Morris would be waiting at San Francisco or Vancouver with a full west-to-east tour booked up for me. In other words I have consistently "worked my passage" on all my tours with the exception of the time spent on ship-board! And even on the long days and weeks at sea I have utilized the time to compose new songs and perfect the ground-plans of others! Two years ago, sailing from India to the Straits Settlements there was a man on board our ship who was always speaking about

"my friend MacKay" and what the two of them would do
when they met. Result—one of my best recent numbers
"When I Meet MacKay." All my sailor songs, including
"There is Somebody Waiting for Me" and a new "Pirate"
song which I am just rounding off have been inspired on
board ship. So you see I am never really idle. Constitution-
ally I seem to be incapable of idleness or laziness of any
description. Ever since the war I have felt that I must be
"up and at it!" all the time.

And America has given me all the hard work that I have
been able to take on during the past few years! Believe me,
I must have been a very strong man indeed to have fulfilled
all the professional responsibilities taken on for me by Mr.
Morris since 1918! During the years that have intervened
since then I have seldom been out of the States for more
than a few months at a time. He has even taken me down
to Mexico. And my last tour was easily the most strenuous
of all. For goodness knows how many weeks I did little else
than play one-night shows. It was a raging, tearing, tireless
campaign throughout most of the States of the Union. How
I did not succumb under the physical pressure I do not know
but this I do know—I will never again take on such a task
for Will Morris or any other man, no matter how tempting
the "rake-off" may be! No, sirs, never no more!

Only in America could any man come through such a
six-months' hustle without a complete bodily and mental collapse. There is, as I have stated earlier in this story, a something in the very air of the country which sustains one and
permits of long-continued exertions which would be impossible under any other than electrical conditions. Besides one
is daily being brought into contact with old friends or new
ones presenting fresh and fascinating types of character.
And here it occurs to me that it might not be out of place
to make a few very brief references to some of the better-
known men and women I have met in the course of my

American travels. I have already given you my personal impressions of the various Presidents during the past twenty years—all extraordinary men. But the United States is full of extraordinary men.

At one time or another I have met most of the leading industrial magnates from the late Andrew Carnegie down to the redoubtable Henry Ford. Mr. Carnegie I met first in my dressing-room at Blaney's Theatre and afterwards I visited him by invitation at his house in Fifth Avenue, the most sumptuous home I have ever been inside in my life. "Andrew" and I had many long talks about his old home town of Dumfermline and his Scottish castle of Scibo. He was particularly anxious that I should visit the Homestead Works at Pittsburgh and gave me letters of introduction to, among others of his colleagues and managers, Mr. Charlie Schwab. At a later date I was able to visit and inspect the enormous and terrifying plant at the famous steel town of Pennsylvania. Mr. Carnegie always appealed to me as a simple and kindly man, but preternaturally shrewd in industrial and financial affairs. His name will live as long as the higher education of young Scotsmen lasts in the universities of my native land. Already, by his benefactions to these institutions, he has enabled thousands of our boys to equip themselves for the battle of life with the best education the world affords.

Mr. Henry Ford came down one evening to the Shubert Theatre in Detroit when I was performing there. He came "behind" subsequently and assured me that I had made him laugh more heartily than he had done for many years. I replied that we were equal in this respect for I had laughed more over Ford car stories than at any other joke which had ever been invented. This pleased him immensely. He came to our hotel next day and drove my wife and I out to his works in the first Ford sedan produced from the famous Detroit plant. My wife admired the little car so much

SIR HARRY AND GOVERNOR AL. SMITH OF NEW YORK

that Mr. Ford said he would send her one to Dunoon. He did so but forgot to send a chassis with the sedan so I had to purchase one in Manchester on our return to England! Let me say at once that it was a grand little bus and we ran it all over Argyllshire for several years. I have also met Mr. Edsell Ford. He is a real "chip of the old block" a worthy son of a worthy father. I shall always be proud of having shaken hands with Henry Ford who, in my opinion, is well entitled to be included among any list of America's really great and illustrious men. Two other men associated with the motor industry in the States with whom I was on friendly terms were the Dodge brothers—both wonderful fellows with hearts as big as their bodies.

I have referred to Mr. "Charlie" Schwab in connection with his old chief Andrew Carnegie. Mr. Schwab I met on more than one occasion and formed the opinion of him that he was a strong, dominating, but honest and fearless personality; the sort of man to depend on in any emergency and who would carry through any scheme or ideal he had set his heart upon once he had made up his mind that it was the right and wise thing to do. I have been brought into personal contact with the Swifts, the Armours, and with the great warehouse kings like Marshall Field and the late John Wanamaker. I was one of the few stage celebrities that Mr. Wanamaker came to hear in Philadelphia. He was always exceedingly kind to me and my wife and we were accorded the great privilege of visiting him in his private rooms at the famous stores which bear his name. He was loved by everybody who knew him and by none more so than his thousands of employees. If I had to describe John Wanamaker in a few words I should say he was a thoroughly good Christian man.

Naturally I have met all the great fighting men of the States from old John L. Sullivan down to the present champion, Gene Tunney. Gene and I have the same theatrical manager, Will Morris, and only a few weeks ago, in Chicago,

Gene, Will, Tom, and I dined together and swapped stories. This was before the second meeting with Dempsey had been arranged but Gene was supremely confident of retaining his crown no matter when or where the return battle took place. Tunney is a magnificent specimen of manhood with a mentality considerably above and beyond the majority of professional pugilists I have met. I tried him out by asking if he had ever heard of a man named Robert Burns. Secretly I would have laid ten bucks to one that he would correct me and say "Of course you mean Tommy Burns!" But I was wrong. At once Gene came back at me with

> "Had we never loved so kindly
> Had we never loved so blindly,
> Never met and never parted
> We had ne'er been broken-hearted!"

—and I had to hand it to him for the smart literary boy with a knowledge of real poetry.

"John L." I first saw in Boston many years ago but he was then an old man and had been in retirement from the ring for a very long time. He attended several of my performances and always came round to the dressing-room for a chat. I suppose that John L. has turned in his grave several times on hearing of the colossal sums recently earned by the masters of the ring in America. It was at Boston, I remember, that I was the central figure in a very awkward incident over which I have often laughed since but which was no laughing matter for me at the time. I had gone with several friends to the Boston Athletic Club to see the late Jim Driscoll fight a lad named Grover Hayes. As I did not want to attract undue publicity I put on an old cap and turned up my coat collar before going into the club. The fight was so fascinating and lasted so long that I forgot all about the time. Suddenly looking at my watch I discovered to my horror that it was ten minutes after the hour of my performance at the theatre. So I made a break-neck dash out

CHARLIE CHAPLIN AND SIR HARRY AT LOS ANGELES
They have Exchanged Hats and Sticks

of the club and got on the stage almost half an hour late.
Fortunately—as I imagined at the time—the manager had
gone on and apologized for my absence on the plea that I
had been engaged in a charity performance in a distant part
of the city. But next morning the papers came out with a
full report of the manager's remarks and, in another column,
a story of how keenly interested Harry Lauder had been
in the Driscoll-Hayes fight! I tell you I had to suffer many
leg-pulls about my interest in charity performances in
Boston!

Jim Corbett I often met in different cities all over the
States. The last time I saw Jim I had to congratulate him
on the success of his reminiscences in the columns of the
great periodical in which my own recollections have also
appeared. "The Roar of the Crowd" certainly held my
breathless attention for many weeks. I regard the story as a
ring classic of the first water. Jim Corbett has always been
in a class by himself both as a fighter and as a personality.
Both Jim Jeffries and Jack Dempsey I have met in Los
Angeles frequently, while dear old Bob Fitzsimmons first
came into my ken by stepping on to a New York stage in my
early days and handing me a decorated horse-shoe which he
had forged himself and bearing a card on which were the
words "From One Champ to Another!" In the dressing-room
afterwards Bob gave an exhibition of the hit which floored
Jim Corbett in their famous fight and he was so realistic
that Tom pulled me away from the old fire-eater in dread
that he would forget himself and imagine that I was his
opponent of ten years before.

When playing Los Angeles I have had the pleasure of
seeing most of the world's cinema stars. My greatest friend
in Hollywood is Charlie Chaplin. Every time I go there he
and I foregather and many a crack and palaver we have about
the old days when he was a comedian, like myself, on the
British stage. Well do I remember Charlie (although I didn't

know his name then) and his grotesque antics in Fred
Karno's funny sketches. Often, when a Karno production
was on the same bill as myself, would I go round to the front
of the house and chuckle with merriment at the drolleries
of the little black-haired fellow with the red nose and the
wobbly body movements. Charlie comes to the theatre to see
me and I go "on the lot" to see him. We have been photographed a score of times together. One picture in particular
which always makes my friends laugh when I let them see
it is entitled Charlie Lauder and Harry Chaplin. In it we
have changed costumes and the result is a really comical
picture.

Among many other personal friends I have at Hollywood
are Douglas Fairbanks, Harold Lloyd, Will Hart, Fred
Niblo, Reginald Denny, John Gilbert, and Joe Schenck. Of
the movie queens I know specially well, Mary Pickford,
Gloria Swanson, Edna Purviance, Mary Miles Minter, Bessie
Love, and the Talmadge girls are the chief and I must give
them all credit for being exceedingly nice to a poor legitimate actor and singer like myself who has to work hard for a
mere pittance of the enormous salaries they earn as silver
screen favourites. I vastly enjoy my occasional visits to Los
Angeles and film-land. Its inmates are most lovable people,
warm-hearted, gay and careless of everything save their work
which they take very seriously indeed. I have spent many
charming days and interesting evenings among the hierarchy
of the cinema world in sunny Los Angeles. Some day I
would like very much to go out there and make a picture
myself.

CHAPTER TWENTY-TWO

BAD TIPS AND OTHERS

ONE of the most fascinating men I ever met in the States was Joseph Smith, the head of the Mormons in Salt Lake City. When I first visited that amazing city many years ago Joseph came with his "retinue" to hear my entertainment. He came to my dressing-room after the show and we had a long and interesting talk. I was so impressed with the intelligence and the dignity of the man that I restrained my inclination to ask him any of the questions that would naturally occur to a Scottish Presbyterian reared within the strict laws and "commandments" of that rather rigid faith. Like many more people I had, from early youth upwards, harboured certain sentiments about the Mormons, their beliefs and practices, which tended to make my inaugural trip to their headquarters one of no little curiosity. But when I really had the chance, at first hand, so to speak, to make direct inquiries into a much-discussed topic, I somehow let it slip—I simply could not bring myself to open a series of questions on what my visitor might reasonably have regarded as purely domestic affairs!

So instead we talked of Salt Lake City itself, its magnificent situation, its noble buildings, its civic activities, its happy, prosperous citizens. Mr. Smith told me that there were many Scottish people resident in the city, a large proportion of them members of the Mormon Church. I said I was not at all astonished at the news as I knew many men who were Mormons in Scotland! As he didn't even smile at this attempted witticism on my part I passed on to discuss with him the really extraordinary history of the city from the far-off days when the seagulls came and devoured the locusts that were threatening to starve the ancient settlers down to the present time. He told me that there never were any unemployed people in Salt Lake and gave me many more interesting details about a city which must be absolutely unique in the United States to say nothing of the world as a whole. I have returned to Salt Lake City frequently since these days and I am a great favourite there I can assure you. But I have not yet got inside the wonderful Temple to hear a religious service. Admission is strictly limited to "the faithful" and much as I would like to see its internal beauties and listen to its services I do not propose at my time of life to become a Mormon in order that I may do so.

In the old days of Brigham Young and his "elders" the foundation and the building of Salt Lake City must have been gigantic tasks. Just fancy! They took forty-two years to build the Temple alone and all the stones for it were cut from a quarry forty miles distant and transported under conditions of great difficulty mostly on the backs of the men who helped to construct the now world-famous edifice. I shall always say that no matter what "ongoin's" may have taken place in the early days of Salt Lake City the pioneers of Mormonism were men of supreme vision, of indominatable pluck, of astounding ability as architects and builders. Their descendants today are no whit less able; I defy you to find, in all the States of the Union, a better conducted or more civically enlightened city than Salt Lake.

Another prominent American "character" who adorns my list of personal friends is Mayor William Hale Thompson of Chicago. This solemn pronouncement on my part will probably cause a gasp of horror on the part of numerous good Americans, both in Chicago and elsewhere, to whom the mere name of "Bill" Thompson is anathema. But I cannot help it. I like Bill immensely. He and I always have a jolly good time together in "Chi." Nobody would accuse

TOM VALLANCE, SIR HARRY, CHARLIE CHAPLIN, AND SYD CHAPLIN 'ON THE LOT' AT HOLLYWOOD

him of being pro-British in his spoken sentiments or in his
actions but he is certainly pro-Lauder and he hands me the
keys of the Windy City every time I set foot in it. I was
much amused at some of the things my friend the Mayor
gave utterance to during his last election fight and equally
entertained by some of the things his enemies hurled back at
him in the columns of the anti-Thompson press. My friend
Blackwood went over to America a year or two ago and lined
up one day at the city chambers with a letter of introduction
from me to William Hale T.

"Tell this guy that if he's a Scotsman I'll see him; if he's
an Englishman show him out and put a detective on him
while he's in Chicago!" was the Mayor's ultimatum to the
messenger. On being told that Blackwood was a Scot, Bill
had him shown to his room at once. They became very
friendly and were getting along fine when Bill learned that
Blackwood was a journalist. As one of the Chicago papers
had that morning roasted the Mayor unmercifully over some
alleged misfealty or another this information suddenly
caused him to see red and the interview was on the point of
coming to an abrupt conclusion. However Bill thought better
of it and, holding out his hand, he remarked, with that smile
of his which can be so attractive when he likes, "As a friend
of Harry's I'll tell the woild you're welcome to this great
and progressive City, but as a journalist I hate the —— sight
of you!" The Mayor, and his Chief of Police, Mr. Charlie
Fitzmaurice gave Blackwood such a good time in Chicago
that he spent a week there instead of, as he had first intended,
a couple of days. William Hale Thompson provides the
people of Britain with many a good laugh, especially when
he really gets down to his anti-English stuff which, of
course, nobody believes in for a moment. I don't believe
"dear old Bill" believes in it himself!

I was often told by my friends that America has been
very good to me. And occasionally, if I seem to be in a com-

municative humour, one or other of these friends will try
to do the pump-handle trick and ask me just how much
money I have made in the States and Canada. "Oh, I haven't
done so badly," I tell them always, "and I would have done
still better had I been able to stick to a' I earned—the livin'
oot there's awfu' costly!" And there is a slight substratum
of truth in part, at least, of that canny reply. I defy any
man to keep on going to America as I have done for twenty
years and not make a financial sideslip now and again. At
heart I am a very simple man and though I have steeled
myself against "easy-money" all my life—realizing that the
only money worth having is the money you have worked
hard for—I was very prone in my earlier visits to the States
to listen to all sorts of tales and schemes having for their
object the quick and certain collecting of dollars either in
hundreds or tens of thousands! I suppose my reputation for
excessive caution in matters monetary kept away from me
many people who would otherwise have been only too pleased
to enlist my sympathies and my bank-book in certain get-
rich-quick Wallingford plans. But I couldn't steer clear of
them all! And as this more than purports to be a real story
of my life it would not be fair of me to let my friends
everywhere assume that I had never been "trimmed."

Many years ago, during, I think, my first visit to Boston
I fell across the path of a most fascinating young man who
could speak in nothing less than millions of dollars. He had
worked up a trans-continental reputation at an age in life
when most lads are thinking of how they are going to pay
the next instalment on their bicycles. The papers had a lot
to say about him; he was very much in the public eye all
over the States. If I told you his popular nick-name many of
my readers would remember him and his highly spectacular
doings but by-gones are by-gones with me and I have no
desire to rake up old troubles in the case of a man who may
still be alive and earning an honest living. Well, this young

sprig got me going from the first time I was introduced
to him. I used to listen pop-eyed to his patter about the
enormous sums he had made for his clients. And not for a
long time did he even suggest that I should employ his inval-
uable services in any capacity whatever. In fact it began to
be very clear to me that I was ten times a fool for not
handing over my entire wad to this genius and letting him
multiply it a thousand times overnight. Every time he came
to see me and started to spin his amazing yarns I went all
dizzy at the thought of what I was missing.

Then one nice winter morning he drove up to the door
of the Parker House Hotel in Boston in a gorgeous two-
horse sleigh. That did it. Any man who could sport such a
slap-up turnout was bound to be making money for himself
as well as his fortunate clients. He took me for a ride over
the snow and to the music of the tinkling bells on his horses'
collars I fell for a scheme which was to make me a multi-
millionaire in three weeks' time. All the "wise guys" in
New York, Boston, Philadelphia, and Chicago were supposed to be in the plunder; we were each going to have a
rake-off that would make my weekly salary sound like a
taxi-fare! We dined later (at his expense) at the Algonquin
Club—and I passed over my cheque. That's the end of the
story. Years afterwards I learned that the sleigh-man got
five years' solid for fraud and I was really sorry to hear it,
for he was a clever young devil and he "had" me good and
hearty.

Another time I was introduced through a friend to a
man in New York who was reputed to have invented a synthetic rubber which was going to put all the rubber plantations of the world out of business. It was just about the
time of a sensational rubber boom. Everybody was talking
rubber. Fortunes were being made in the commodity. Henry
Ford, the Dodge Brothers, Willys and all the rest of the
car manufacturers were (so it was adroitly pushed into me)

seriously thinking of paying this man a fabulous amount of money for his patent; if they didn't do something desperate a set of rubber tires was soon going to cost more than the cars they manufactured! Of course if I was *really* interested and cared to pick up half a million or so of quick money there would be no trouble in letting a prominent man and a good old guy like Harry Lauder in on the ground floor. And so forth. For a long while I resisted the temptation. But when the inventor came along to my dressing-room one evening and produced a great chunk of his synthetic rubber which looked like rubber, felt like rubber, tasted like rubber (I broke a false tooth on it so keen was I to test it in every way) and, most wonderful of all, "bounced" like rubber, my last scruples went by the board. I walked right in. Never mind how much; I hate to think about it. Fancy any man not recognizing a bit of real rubber when he saw it, felt it, tasted it and bounced it! But it's always the simplest trick that gets away with the applause—and the sucker's money.

A coal mine in Mexico was the next thing out of which I tried hard to turn an honest penny. It belonged to an Englishman who was one of the most earnest liars I have ever met. He must have studied up all the mining jargon and technicalities before he started his barrage so far as I was concerned because he had them all so pat that I, as an ex-miner, was interested in spite of myself. There were the photographs of the mine-shaft and the miners' houses and groups of happy children! Here were other photographs of the loaded wagons at the railway siding and groups of sturdy miners going to and coming from their work. Here was the last letter from the local manager saying how well everything was going and just what the little company could do if they had some more capital to extend their activities by sinking another shaft to a wonderful seam a mile away! There would be no difficulty, naturally, in raising ten times the necessary money in the district where the mine was sit-

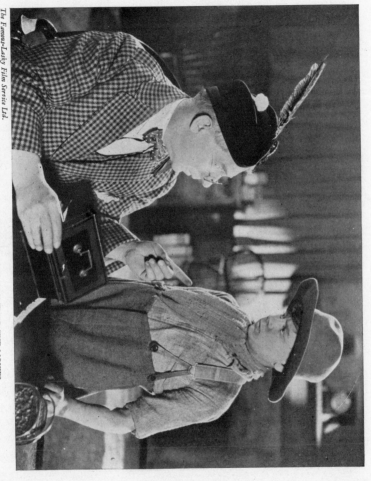

A SCENE FROM "HUNTINGTOWER," WHEN SIR HARRY TRIED THE MOVIES

uated and where the quality of its coal was so much appreciated but, well, what a sensation it would cause down in Mexico if Harry Lauder, the old miner, agreed to go on the board of directors! And if I thought I would like to invest a few thousand dollars just for fun, why, everybody would be tickled to death! Besides, it would be money for jam! I never saw a dollar of my five thousand come back from that Mexican coal-mine. Years after, when I was down in the country, I made some inquiries about it. Yes, there used to be a coal-mine at the place mentioned or at least a half-bored shaft but that was thirty years ago and the Englishman who owned it hadn't been seen since. Was there a railway near it? No, the nearest railroad was ten miles away. I often wonder how many other people were taken in completely by that glib-tongued mine-proprietor and his collection of faked photographs of happy miners and forged letters from the local manager!

Over in England, too, where people are not so ready to fall for the fortune-while-you-sleep talk I have been prevailed upon to dip down for goodly sums on what looked like hundred per cent stone certainties. A very good friend of mine—and we are still friendly, mark you, but in a rather aloof way now—put me off my sleep for a few nights conning over the possibilities of a new engine which could be fitted for a few pounds to sailing fishing yawls and thus let them make for the harbour quickly with their scaly spoil. The scheme seemed sound as a bell. Fish, I argued to myself, were always worth money if they could be brought to market but they were of no use whatever lying in the bottom of an Auchmithie fishing-smack. And wouldn't I be doing a kind turn to the poor fishermen by providing them with engines—at a profit, of course—so that they could get back at once to their bonnie wee harbours without having to worry about wind or tide! The engine was to be called the Harry Lauder Fisherman's Friend. Yes, the scheme was fool-proof and bound to succeed. But neither the originator of the stunt nor myself paused to think that not three per cent of the British fish consumed by our population was landed by fishing boats of the dear old brown-sailed type. And that even if we fitted our engine to every "cobble" on the east coast of Scotland we would still be out of pocket on the deal. In any case the engine didn't work when we did start our engineering business. And that was the end of it—our company went broke!

Later, I became a part-proprietor in a Leeds concern which was to turn out suits of clothes for fifteen shillings ($3.50) a suit. Clothes in Britain were far too dear. Working people could not afford to dress themselves decently because of the exhorbitant profits snatched by the greedy tailors. This ought to be put a stop to. We would stop it—and in stopping it clean up a dollar a suit on a million suits a year. Money for nothing! We actually turned out some thousands of suits but the public wouldn't look at them. Having tried to wear one of the suits myself I don't blame them. The company failed. For months afterwards I could not pass a tailor's shop without feeling a pain in the stomach!

But all my financial transactions outside my legitimate business have not turned out failures. Andrew Carnegie one night came to my dressing-room in New York. He was astonished and delighted to meet in me a man smaller than himself and said so with great glee. I denied that I was shorter in stature than he and we decided to settle the argument by measuring heights against the dressing-room door. Before Andrew took up his position for Tom to take his height he said that if he beat me he would give me a good tip on the Stock Exchange. Overhearing this I think Tom decided there and then that the steel magnate would win. In any case Tom gave the verdict in favour of Mr. Carnegie by a tenth of an inch. "Buy United States Steel Common!" whispered the millionaire on saying goodnight. Next day

The Famous-Lasky Film Service Ltd.
IN "HUNTINGTOWER"

The Famous-Lasky Film Service Ltd.
A CHARACTER PART IN "HUNTINGTOWER"

I bought a thousand at thirty-two dollars and forgot all about the transaction for several weeks; in fact I was back in London before Steel Common were brought to my memory by hearing some fellows speak about them. "What are they standing at today?" I asked excitedly. Round about forty-two I was told. I couldn't get to the nearest telephone quick enough to order my broker to sell my lot. Almost without a halt those Steel Common went to something over a hundred dollars and every day for months after I sold out I didn't know whether to laugh or cry.

It was the same with Marconi shares. A very "knowledg-able" magnate whom I was friendly with during an Atlantic voyage spoke about little else than Marconi's throughout the trip and prognosticated for them a most wonderful rise in value. I bought a tidy little packet at $3.25 the day after I landed in England. Soon they began to move in the right direction and when they got the length of $4.20 I again decided that the margin of profit was ample for any man who was not of a grasping disposition. I consulted my banker on the matter of these Marconi's before parting with them. Cautious Scot that he was, he strongly urged me to sell and leave any additional profit to the man who bought them. "Never object, Harry, to the other chap getting a slice of the melon as well as yourself!" was how he put it. I sold. "The other man, whoever he was, got something over twenty dollars a share for his "slice of the melon" where I got one and once more I started to count up the money I had "lost"! These were the only two actual transactions I ever had on the Stock Exchange and I don't suppose I shall ever have another. It's too nerve-wracking when you don't win as much as you ought to have won!

CHAPTER TWENTY-THREE

SOUTH AFRICA

IN 1920 I went to South Africa under the direction of Ted Carroll. On the steamer going out was the late Lord Leverhulme, the British millionaire who started life as a small grocer somewhere in the Midlands and ended up by being one of the greatest industrial magnates in the world, employing tens of thousands of people and controlling many millions of capital. His lordship and I had many interesting chats as we promenaded the decks or lay in our chairs enjoying the breeze of the north and south Atlantic. Like so many men who have risen in the world by their own unaided efforts he was inclined to be masterful in his manner and outlook. He was keen to know all about my early struggles; I remember him saying that nothing was more fascinating to him than stories of the personal conflict, by which I suppose he meant the early struggles of men who had made good in their own particular careers. And he amused me very much by telling me that my name was quite familiar to him but he had never heard me on the stage—he had never had the time!

I asked Leverhulme if he thought that success was a matter of good fortune or determination. He replied that he was firmly convinced that every man was given his chance at one time or another but that success, in the ordinary sense of the word, might be regarded in different ways by different people. Far too much store, he urged, was put on financial success. The man who spent a lifetime trying to invent some new process for the betterment of industry and succeeded in the end; the author who took twenty years to produce a masterpiece of literature; or the doctor who devoted his life to the battle against yellow fever over there—nodding his head in the direction of what used to be called the White Man's Grave in Africa—all scored successes in life against which the acquired millions of a commercial potentate or a financier counted as very little indeed. The trouble is, went on his lordship, that people today place far too much store on purely material success. "You yourself do not go all over the world today singing and acting purely for the money you earn—am I not right?" I confessed, as any man faced with such a question has to confess, that there is something above and beyond the monetary rewards of individual success whether you are a soap-merchant, a bridge-builder, a warehouseman or a comedian—"Yes," I replied, "I do it because I like doing it; it's my work and if you like your work you enjoy it all the more when the pay is good!" Lord Leverhulme laughed at this sally of mine, remarking that the philosophy of it was unanswerable up to a point. I could see, however, that his thoughts and mine on the subject of success marched pretty closely together—the fight is the great thing in life if in that fight you do not trample on other people, if your personal triumphs, your acquisition of wealth or power do not spell misery and oppression to others. I told his lordship of an old man I knew in a London suburb who made barely enough to live on but who spent all his time making ships' models and whose dearest aim in life was to leave behind him the most perfect model of an Elizabethan warship in the world. "Did he do it?" asked Lord Leverhulme. "He did," I replied. "Then he was one of the world's most successful men!" said Lord Leverhulme, and we went below for lunch.

This talk of ours on success came back to my mind forcibly on the day of our arrival at Cape Town. I was accorded a most wonderful reception on stepping off the gangway and en route to my hotel. Many, many thousands of people assembled to see and cheer me. The Cape Town police, on their famous white chargers, were all on duty; the newspaper reporters were out in full force. It seemed to me that the famous city at the foot of Table Mountain had gone on holiday to greet Harry Lauder. The scenes reminded me of my first visit to Sydney in Australia—they were overwhelmingly enthusiastic and I kept asking myself what I had done to deserve a welcome so cordial and so spectacular. Later I was told that the returning South African generals who had played such a magnificent part in the great war and in the subsequent peace negotiations in Paris, London, and elsewhere had not been given so wildly colourful a reception as I had received. Instead of pleasing me this information rather saddened me but I comforted myself with the reflection that there are lots of things in life that are unequal and rather difficult to understand! Lord Leverhulme and Harry Lauder stepped off the same boat; the former drove to his hotel with one or two personal attendants and friends. I had to play the actor's part to perhaps fifty thousand smiling, hat-waving, huzzaing men, women, and children. I leave it at that.

My opening week at Cape Town saw the theatre stormed every night by far more people than could get into the house. Those who did get in gave me tremendously warm receptions. I had to sing so many songs that the acts of the other performers had to be "cut" almost to vanishing point; most evenings I was "on" for the better part of two hours. One night early in the week the Governor General, Lord Buxton, came with his entourage and occupied the principal stage box. At the end of my performance I went over and shook hands with his lordship. He warmly returned my greeting and invited me to call on him at Government House the next day. This incident caused a great deal of talk in Cape Town. Nothing like it had ever been heard of in South Africa before. The idea of an entertainer presuming to act in this familiar manner with the representative of His

Majesty the King shocked certain people but all I know
is that the audience shouted themselves hoarse with delight
and that I was constrained to do what I did by the very
evident enjoyment my "turn" gave to his excellency the
Governor.

Cape Town is a fine city with a truly magnificent situation. There are many lovely drives all round the district and
almost every day I motored out to places of picturesque or
historic interest including Groote Schuur, the noble mansion
house and grounds presented by the late Cecil Rhodes to be a
permanent residence for the reigning Prime Minister of
South Africa. I do not think I have ever been in a finer
house anywhere in the world—and certainly not in one more
gloriously placed or with a better view. Having a profound
admiration for Rhodes and his wonderful career I naturally
went to see this famous man's tomb when I got north to
Buluwayo. It is the most solemnly impressive burial-place
in the world. Away up in the bleak wilderness of the Ma-
toppo Hills, surrounded by giant boulders which must have
been thrown skywards by a gigantic upheaval too terrible
for the mind to contemplate, Cecil Rhodes, empire-builder,
sleeps his last lonely sleep. He selected his own grave.
Rhodes may have been ruthless in many ways but he had
great vision and immense courage and his imprint on South
Africa will last for ever.

Our tour took us to all the States in the Union and to
every city and town of any size in Cape Town, the Trans-
vaal, the Free State, and Natal. In Johannesburg I played
for a full month. The demand for seats was so excessive in
this city that record prices were charged and I remember
Ted Carroll handing me a series of weekly checks which
—well, which read a whole lot better to me than writs for
debt! It was at the end of my inaugural week at Jo'burg
that my manager passed over to me the biggest check I had
ever taken for a week's work in my life up till then. How

much did it represent? I can hear some of you ask. I'd hate
to tell you. But I ear-marked it for a new Rolls Royce on
my return home! Mind you, I had no compunction about
charging the Jews in Johannesburg for the privilege of
hearing me because the Jews like to give money to Scotsmen.
And I should think that two-thirds of the inhabitants of
the city are of the ancient faith. I met many of them and
they were all very kind to me. At the hotel where I was
living a well-known member of the race kept me in fits of
laughter telling me stories against his own people.

"I suppose, Sir Harry," he said to me one afternoon
after lunch, "you think that the gold industry is the chief
business in Jo'burg? Vell, you're wrong. It's bankruptcy!
There are more people go bankrupt out here than in any
other city in the world. The trade in bankruptcy is very
flourishing. Did you ever hear the story about the two Jews
in Jo'burg who were drawing up articles of partnership
before their lawyer? No! Vell, the lawyer goes all over the
articles before the final signing and suddenly says, 'But there
are no mentions of fire or bankruptcy—I have made a mistake, these must go in!' 'Quite right,' says the partners speaking at once. 'Put them in but the profits are equal in both
cases!' "

Some years ago, I believe, a League of Gentiles was
formed in Johannesburg with the avowed object of curtailing
the powers and the prominence of the Jews. So far as I
was able to judge this league had not made any substantial
progress up till the time of my visit. New York and Jo'burg
seem to me to be the Jerusalems of the modern world. I
don't know what we Scots are going to do about it, speaking
generally, that is. But I have certainly done *my* duty in both
places by taking pretty substantial toll from the Israelites
within their borders!

One of the greatest compliments I have ever received

was paid me in Johannesburg. The Kaffirs were tremendously anxious to hear me and would have paid any prices to be admitted to the theatre. But in South Africa the colour line is drawn very strictly. So the natives drew up a petition, or, at all events appointed a deputation to see my manager and ask that I should give performances at which natives only would be present. The idea was to take a hall somewhere and give one or two special matinees. This request so touched me that I expressed my willingness to entertain "Kaffirs only" if a sufficiently large hall could be secured for the purpose. But certain difficulties presented themselves and the scheme fell through. Later I visited one or two of the principal compounds and encampments and spent a few very pleasant and amusing hours with the Kaffirs and their chiefs. They are fine upstanding fellows—splendid physical specimens every man of them. Writing about the natives of South Africa reminds me that at Burban I met a Basuto doctor whose command of English was considerably better than my own. In fact he amazed me by his polished and fluent talk. He knew all about me and my career. I asked him in considerable astonishment how this came about. "Oh," he replied, "I was educated at Edinburgh and often heard you sing in the good old Empire in Nicholson Street!" He added that he had a full collection of my records in his home and that occasionally he took his gramaphone to the hospital with which he was connected and played my tunes to the patients. There must, I think be something "international" in my voice or my manner of singing that makes a strange appeal to the peoples of all races for I have met Chinese, Japanese, Maories, Philippinos, Red Indians, and even Esquimaux who are familiar with my records and enjoy my tunes though they don't all understand the words. It is extraordinary and I have long given up trying to explain it even to myself.

I have never been back to South Africa but I have had many warm invitations to return and when, perhaps twenty years from now, I really set out on my positively final farewell tour of the world I must renew the pleasant acquaintance of the interesting folks of that fascinating land!

CHAPTER TWENTY-FOUR

THE ORIENT

WRITING about South Africa and my restless indulgence in travel generally recalls to my mind rather an interesting fact. And it is this—I once played in no fewer than twenty of the world's principal cities within the space of twelve months. Beginning in America with San Francisco, I came east to Chicago, Detroit, New York, Boston, and Philadelphia, then went north to Montreal and Winnipeg; sailed home and played London, Manchester, Liverpool, Glasgow and Edinburgh. October saw me on my way to India's coral strand—an old hymn-book phrase which has never quite left my mind. Although I played practically all the Indian cities I only include Calcutta in this list; later I found myself in Hongkong and Shanghai. Then down to Singapore in the Straits Settlements (or, to give them their right title the Federated Malay States) and so on to Sydney, Melbourne, and Adelaide. If any artiste in the world can beat this little record he is welcome. Not a bad year's "sight-seeing" you will admit. And everywhere I went I did a job of work just to keep the pot boiling, if you understand me. I always say that a man enjoys touring the world far better when he is able to pick up his bite and sup as he goes along! And if, luckily, he comes home with a shilling or two in his waistcoat pocket so much the better still!

This trip of mine to the Orient I had long and keenly looked forward to. I wanted to see whether the Mediterranean was really blue; I wanted to sail down the Red Sea —slit in two so that the Israelites could make their escape "out of the house of bondage"; I wanted to set foot in India, that storied land of mystery and romance first focussed

265

on my mind by the vivid essays of Tom Macaulay on Lord Clive and Warren Hastings. How I had longed, as a boy, to have the opportunity of viewing the "barren rocks of Aden" (subject of one of our very best and liveliest bappipe tunes); of gazing on the peerless Taj Mahal at Agra; of wandering in historic Lucknow and noting the road by which "brave Havelock and His Highlanders" came to the rescue of the beleagured Britishers at the time of the Mutiny; of seeing the "dawn come up like thunder out o' China 'cross the bay." Well, all these dreams were realized on this trip of mine in 1925.

Earlier in these memoirs I think I said that I would like to write a book about Australia. I would like even better to write a book about India. But the objections I perceived in writing about Australia would hold quite as pointedly in any serious attempt on my part to write about India. So I will only give you some fragmentary impressions of my experiences in, and my thoughts on, the most fascinating country in all the world.

I started my Indian tour at Bombay. The moment I stepped on the stage for my first performance I sensed the eternal glamour of the East. The house was crowded from floor to ceiling. Hundreds of beautiful Parsee ladies were in the stalls and circle. Their picturesque dress and their flashing jewels helped to make up a scene the like of which I had never beheld from the stage of any theatre in the world. It almost took my breath away by its sheer colourfulness and opulence. Even while I was singing my mind was flitting back to the pages of the Arabian Nights. And if the scene inside the theatre made such an impression on me what can I say of my first visit to the home of a great Indian prince, the Nizam of Hyderabad? This famous and enlightened potentate has, I believe, many stately palaces but none can surely be more lovely than that which he has on Malabar Hill on the outskirts of, and above, Bombay! Lady

Lauder and I were invited to dinner there. We thought we had indeed been transplanted into fairyland with all its perfect embellishments of glinting moonbeams, waving palms, gorgeous flowers and multi-coloured electric lights. It was so amazingly wonderful that we were almost afraid to speak —and break the spell!

The Governor of Bombay, Sir Leslie Wilson, invited us to the Residency; indeed everywhere we went in India I was royally entertained and could not have made the acquaintance of this romantic land under better conditions. At Calcutta I attended the Christmas Party given by the Earl of Reading, the Viceroy, and also had the satisfaction of backing the winner of the Viceroy's Cup at the Races. Orange William, the horse in question, was favourite and I remember how very disappointed I was at only getting a few rupees in return for the half-crown I had invested after being assured that William was a "dead cert." This was the only time in my life that I gambled on a race-course so I can say with truth that I have never yet backed a loser!

From Bombay we sailed north to Karachi and then by railroad across the great Sind Desert to Quetta, then down to Lahore, Delhi, Agra, Lucknow, and Cawnpore. At each of these places I played in the evenings and devoted my days to wandering round the city and studying Indian life at close quarters. And an altogether fascinating study this is. The inscrutability of a million years is in every solemn face one sees. Occasionally one meets with a smile—as, for instance, when I slipped up one sultry afternoon on an unusually muddy bit of the Ganges at Benares and very nearly tumbled into the Sacred River—but, speaking generally, the natives are mostly of a grave and serious mien. Time doesn't seem to count with them at all. They are never in a hurry. They take life very leisurely indeed.

Yet they can work to beat the band when necessary. Give the shoemaker, the tailor, or the shirtmaker, or the dressmaker—they will turn up at your bedroom door in the hotel, from nowhere it would seem, immediately you have told the head porter that you want their services—an article to copy and it will be returned to you in a few hours with its new replica down to the last stitch and with shade, shape, and style perfectly reproduced. I have ordered boots and shoes simply by giving an old pair and saying "the same" and been amazed, astounded, at the fidelity of the work and the matching of the material employed. Lady Lauder handed over an old dress as an example of the kind of thing she desired after selecting the silk from which the new garment was to be made. She forgot that in the old one the sleeves had had a slight tuck in them on account of being a trifle too long. Back came the new dress next day with the tucks in the same place and each stitch reproduced in the most exact fashion! One of the male members of our variety party thought he would like a new suit. So he passed over an old one to the trousers of which there had been a slight accident necessitating a patch on the seat. Imagine his horror—and mirth at the same time—when the native suavely presented him with a new suit and triumphantly pointed out how careful he had been to put the patch in the same place as before.

But if the Indians are tremendously slick in making boots, shoes, and wearing apparel they must spend years over some of the exquisite articles they turn out in the way of fine art. At Delhi I purchased several curios in ivory which must have taken the craftsmen who made them incalculable hours, to say nothing of almost inconceivable care. I often take one of these wonderful things into my hands today and speculate as to how it was produced at all—never mind how long it occupied the genius responsible for its existence. It is a carved ivory ornament no bigger than a golf ball but inside it are fourteen other balls all differently carved and each one completely distinct from the other. There is abso-

lutely no crack or join in the outside ball. Now ask yourself
how this is done, by what magic instruments the task must
have been accomplished and how many years the cunning
hands laboured to bring this mystery to perfection!

Lahore is one of the great art-craft centres of India.
Its bazaars are crowded with the output of supreme artistes
in brass, silver, and gold, and inlaid ornaments such as tables,
trays, cigar-boxes, lamps, screens, desk and table decora-
tions. One is lost in profound admiration for the men,
women and boys who give these rare treasures to the world
at prices which appear to be altogether ridiculous in rela-
tion to the work so lovingly, so meticulously, put into them.
I can truthfully say that the bazaars at Lahore are the only
places of merchandise in the world where I have not tried
to beat a salesman down when buying an article that appealed
to me! I hadn't the heart. My own view about these Indian
craftsmen is that they must spend their lives doing the
wonderful work they do for the mere love of creating beautiful things. Their material wants are small. Give them a
handful of rice and they work until they are tired. Then
some more rice and they start all over again. Another rest,
more rice, and more work. What a life! But after all, is ours
any better? I am not certain that it is.

Throughout my travels in India I made constant and
persistent inquiry as to where I could see the famous rope
trick. Like every other man in the world I had heard about
this, the most unique feat in the repertoire of the Eastern
juggler and I would have given a good deal (I can't just
say off-hand how much I *would* have given!) to see this
trick performed before my own eyes. But I met with no
success. Many people told me that they themselves had seen
the performance, or knew people who had, but in all the
months I spent in the country I did not come across one fakir
carrying a rope and attended by a wee black boy. I saw
many snake-charmers, all of whom gave me the creeps by

their uncanny command over deadly cobras and other vipers and I also saw, in Calcutta near the entrance to the Zoological gardens (one of the best zoos in the world, I should say) a fasting man lying on iron spikes which would most assuredly have cut to ribbons any skin not trained to this ordeal from birth, so to speak. But of the world-famous rope-trick—not a vestige.

One most extraordinary thing I did see, however, and this was a fakir at Bombay between whom and a little bird, of the size and colour of a canary, there existed a communion little short of marvellous. The fakir rested with his back against the Gateway of India, the magnificent arch erected at Bombay to commemorate the landing of the King and Queen at the time of the Durbar some years ago, and sent his little feathered companion on repeated journeys through the air to the open windows of the Taj Mahal Hotel opposite. The bird would alight on the window-sill and flutter and bow until the guest inside threw out a coin to its master. This done it would fly back and alight on the latter's shoulder or thumb. Here, in response to music played on a funny mouth instrument by the fakir the bird would perform all manner of quaint and amusing antics. Whenever a head appeared at any of the hotel windows the man would sound some understood note or two on his flute and away went the feathered messenger to ask for alms at close quarters. Between bird and master there appeared to be the most perfect understanding. I watched them for hours and never got tired of a sight so unusual and interesting.

During my stay in Calcutta I was the guest of my old friend Sir Alexander Murray, one of the great merchant princes of India. To his mansion came many of the leading Britishers and Americans in the city and I was splendidly entertained by tales of life, commerce and money-making in Bengal. Several old friendships begun in Scotland were renewed in Calcutta, which is one of the happy hunting-

grounds of Dundee men in search of "siller." The jute industry in Calcutta is closely allied with the same business in
Dundee. In the old days the men from Tayside practically
dominated the jute mills on the banks of the Hooghly and
dozens of great fortunes were made at a time when Indian
labour was much cheaper than it is today. I don't want to
be unkind but I have a suspicion that not a few of the noble
mansions in West Ferry—just outside of Dundee and
reputed to be one of the wealthiest suburbs in the British
Empire—were built, partly, at least, on the results of infant
labour in the jute mills of India. In recent years the jute
profits have not been so large although the war gave many
Dundee men another chance both at home and abroad. But
to their eternal credit be it said hundreds of the young Scots
in India hastened home the minute war broke out and sacri-
ficed fine prospects of fortune for the almost even-money
chance of death or wounds on the field of battle. I knew
quite a number of these gallant Scotto-Indians who went to
France and Flanders to return no more.

His excellency Lord Lyttleton, the Governor of Bengal,
came to the theatre and brought with him their royal high-
nesses Prince and Princess Arthur of Connaught who were
on a visit to the country. They all came to my dressing-
room afterwards and we had a long chat about India and
our various impressions. I told them that if I lived to be
a thousand I could never hope to see a more magnificent
scene than that of the Vice Regal procession to the races
a few days previously. All the colour and romance and mystery of India were concentrated in that pageant of black
and white, red and gold, splendour. And with that remark
I must leave Calcutta.

At Rangoon, where I have several very dear personal
friends, I remained for ten days. This city of the golden
pagodas is the capital of Burma and rich, not only in everything that pertains to the East, but in commerce and industry.

While at Rangoon I had a cordial invitation to visit the palace of Ling Sing, a Chinese gentleman who is known all over India as the Sugar King. He has many other business interests and is reputed to be one of the richest Chinamen in the world. Judging by his home on the outskirts of Rangoon I can easily believe it. It is the last word in Eastern opulence. Mr. Ling Sing—I sincerely hope I am spelling his name correctly—completely knocked the wind out of my sails when I was introduced to him by breaking out with, "Man, Harry, it's a braw, bricht moonlicht nicht, the nicht, is it no? Hooch, aye!" He spoke the Scottish dialect like a native of Stirling. I am not readily "stumped" but I confess that on this occasion I stood and stared "like ony gumph" scarcely crediting the evidence of my ears. Thoroughly enjoying my discomfiture Ling Sing started to laugh and added further to my bewilderment by remarking, "Say, Harry, ma cock, hoo wad ye like me to gie ye a blaw on the pipes—'The seventy-ninth's Farewell' or 'The Haughs o' Cromdale'?" And without further ado he proceeded to seize a set of bagpipes from a table in the corner of the room and "tune up."

I was spell-bound. Sure enough this extraordinary Chinaman started to play the famous air he had first mentioned. Not only so but he began the "waggle walk" of the real Scottish piper. What could I do but jump in behind him and march round, chest expanded, eye flashing, and droning out the melody familiar to me since childhood? Afterwards Ling Sing explained the apparently insoluble mystery. He was not a MacDonald posing as a Chinaman but a genuine native of the Flowery Land. But his father, the original Sugar King, had always had a great admiration for Scots people and when Ling was yet a little boy he was sent to Dollar Academy, in Clackmannanshire, where he remained for several years and absorbed the customs, the language, and the characteristics of his schoolmates so

thoroughly that he was more Scot than anything else by
the time his education was finished and he had (almost
regretfully) to return to the East! I asked him where he
learned to play the pipes. "Oh," he replied, "I was so good
at them that they made me Pipe-Major of the Academy
pipe-band!" And then we sat down to birds'-nest soup and
to eat rice and chicken with chopsticks! On leaving the
palace Ling Sing slapped me on the back and remarked, in
impeccable Scottish accent, "Well, well, Harry, guid nicht
an' joy be wi' ye! It's been like a breath o' the purple heather
to hae ye here. Hastye back again, laddie! Here's to us!
Wha's like us? Damn the yin!" So saying he handed me a
Deoch-an-Doris, took one himself, and Harry Lauder and
Ling Sing, grand Scots both, parted the best of friends and
cronies.

Afterwards, down to the Federated Malay States, perhaps the richest country on the face of the globe. They tell
me that there is sufficient wealth in the Straits Settlements
to pay the British National Debt twice over. In fact I heard
so much of the actual and potential wealth of places like
Penang, Kuala Lumpur, Port Swetenham, and Singapore
that I had serious thoughts of disbanding my company and
starting in on my own in an effort to get a bit before it was
all gone! But I found so many Scotsmen scattered over the
place that I decided the task would be stiffer than it looked
on the surface! You may be pretty sure that if there are
Kemps, and Symes, and McNeills, and Carmichaels, and
Forbes, and McLarens in the Malay States they are not
going to let a newcomer butt in without making him scratch
hard for his whack! Again I listened to what some people
think the most fascinating of human stories—the tales of
poor men who struck the country in past years and got away
with colossal fortunes. The history of the rubber and tin
industries of Malay is full of romance—and, of course, of
tragedy. Take the case of the young Glasgow man who

discovered a tin mine up-country and got several of his
Glasgow friends to finance him in its exploitation. That was
about twenty years ago. Every man who stuck to his original
small holding in the company is now rich beyond the pro-
verbial dreams of avarice—a word I don't like and have
never quite understood! Or the case of the young Tayside
broker in Singapore who has made three fortunes in rubber,
lost them all, and is now building up another. Renang and
Singapore—these have been names to conjure with in financial circles for many years and so far as I am able to judge
the opportunities still offered all over the Malay States are
well worth the attention of young Britishers of determination and the capacity to grasp a chance when it comes along.

I spent many pleasant days on the rubber plantations and
in the tin mining districts in the different States of the
Peninsula and was intensely interested in the men and the
methods employed in both great industries. More than once
I thought how fortunate it was for Britain that she had
a possession like Malay to help us pay our American debts.
Without the world's best tin and rubber territory we might
just as well sign over the British Empire, lock stock and
barrel, to Wall Street—perhaps! And then again—perhaps
not!

From Port Swetenham we sailed along the coast to
Singapore on a lovely little steamer named the *Klang*. The
Captain of this ship was a splendid Highlander of the name
of MacGregor, who courteously welcomed every individual
passenger as he stepped off the gangway on to the deck.
He had such a pronounced accent that I asked him what part
of the Rob Roy-territory he hailed from. "Alas, an' alack,
Sir Harry," he answered. "I have never seen the dear land
of my fathers and my dreams. I was born in New Zealand.
All my life has been spent in these tropical seas. But soon
I hope to retire and the first thing I shall do will be to
go 'home' to Scotland and see the hills and the streams and

the villages my father and mother loved so devotedly."
These words were spoken in the soft, warm accents of the
true Highlander and I could scarcely believe that the speaker
had not been brought up in Callender or Balquidder. He
astonished me still further by telling me that "he had the
full Gaelic" and though my knowledge of this language is
small he was overjoyed when I said a few Gaelic words
to him and volubly answered me in the same tongue. In
his cabin he, like Ling Sing, had a set of bagpipes and he
and I played many a tune on them during the passage. Some
months afterwards I was shocked beyond measure to read
in a New Zealand paper that Captain MacGregor had been
brutally murdered by one of his own crew who had suddenly gone mad. I tell you this story as another example of
the extraordinary way love of country is embedded strong
in the hearts of people of Scottish descent even in cases
where they have never set eyes on the "land of brown heath
and shaggy wood." There is a lump in my throat and a tear
in my eye as I write this little story of Captain MacGregor
of the *S.S. Klang.* I cannot help it. I am not ashamed of it.
The emotion springs from that ineffable, intangible, but tremendously real thing called Scottish sentiment.

Here is another little cameo almost on a par with the
tale of the Gaelic-speaking skipper who had only in his
dreams "beheld the Hebrides." In our variety company we
had a handsome young man called George Greig. He and
his wife played Hawaiian melodies on ukuleles and also sang
duets of life and love in the South Seas. Greig's grandfather
had been a rover in his boyhood, after running away from
school in Aberdeen. Latterly he settled down on Fanning
Island and became the accepted king of that lonely sea-girt
spot of land. He married a full-blooded Hawaiian girl and
they had six sons, on all of whom the father bestowed good
Scottish christian names. When the British Government
wanted to take over Fanning Island for a cable station the

Greig family sold out their rights and they all retired to New Zealand. How George came to join our company as an assisting artiste I don't know but there he was, and speaking good "Scotch" all the time with a slight American accent.

At Shanghai we had to get our passports viséd for Manila. When Tom Vallance went up to the American Consulate for his, Lady Lauder's, and mine, he took George Greig with him. Tom had no trouble, naturally, but when the official came to deal with the copper-coloured Greig certain slight difficulties developed.

"What nationality?" snaps out the official.

"Scottish," promptly responds George.

"Guess you're the first coloured Scot I've met!" comments the Consul's clerk. "Where do you hail from?"

"Fanning Island," says Greig.

"Never heard of it! Where the hell's that?"

"South Pacific!"

"A copper-coloured Scot from Fannin' Island in the South Pacific! Wal, now, can you beat it?" But Greig got his passport and in it his nationality is described as Scottish, much to his satisfaction!

I played Hongkong and Shanghai in China and had great receptions and huge audiences at both places. But the recent Chinese trouble was just breaking out at Shanghai when I struck China so we cut our visit short. Tom saw a lot more of this town than I did because he got in tow with a British detective who promised to give him an exciting time among some of the gambling dens and opium-smoking resorts. Tom assured me that the first tour round was most interesting, the second rather exciting and the third absolutely hair-raising. On the last occasion they hit up against some pretty tidy gun-play. The detective had his hat shot off his head and Tom swears that had he not been a fast runner he would certainly have finished his world-travels in the Chinese quarter of Shanghai that night. In spite of the

British boycott, in full swing about the time of our visit, I did not find the Chinese shopkeepers and hawkers at all unwilling to sell Nance and I all the fancy goods we wanted. We sent home to Dunoon large crates of art-work, ivory and ebony ornaments, bedspreads and other articles which must have taken years of painstaking and amazingly talented labour to produce. I must also hand it to the Chinese shirt and suit-makers as the world's best craftsmen in their own particular spheres of action. Some of the shirts they made for me in Shanghai I am still wearing. They are cool in warm weather and hot in cold weather. I cannot, unfortunately, say the same about their tussore suits. I have half a dozen of these stored away somewhere and will never wear them out unless I go back for long spells to the warm climates for which they are so admirably suited. I must see if I cannot sell them, even at a loss, to some traveller of my stocky build setting sail for the Orient! And I'll throw in my sun-helmet free. Now then, what offers?

I should have visited Yokohama but the appalling earthquake of the year before had practically wiped out the Japanese city and my tour of Asia came to an end with a farewell concert at Kowloon, just across the bay from Hongkong. This is one of the most beautifully situated towns I have ever seen in all my world roamings. There are lots of Scottish and English people both in Hongkong and Kowloon and when I sailed away for Manila hundreds of them assembled on the pier and sang "Will Ye No Come Back Again?"

The Philippine Islands was another part of the world I was most anxious to see and when Ted Carroll was mapping out my Eastern trip I told him to make certain of taking in Manila. He did so and the result was a most interesting ten days in America's greatest overseas possession. Like many more people I had imagined the Philippines to be a few small islands somewhere—it really did not matter where!—between China and Australia. I knew that cigars came from there and that was about all! Actually there are over three thousand islands in the group with a total area of something like a hundred and twenty thousand square miles—almost as big as Great Britain and Ireland even throwing in the Isle of Man, the Channel Islands and the Greater and Lesser Cumbrae in the Firth of Clyde! I tell you it was an eye-opener to me because I thought that all the worth-while islands in the world belonged to us! The city of Manila, with its quarter of a million inhabitants, fascinated me greatly by reason of its lovely buildings, luxurious hotels, and the almost eternal sunshine in which it is bathed. American enterprise and American capital have done much to develop the Philippines but the thing which has done more for the islanders themselves than any other is the fact that they bred a world's champion boxer in the late Pancho Villa!

We went one night to the local Stadium where we saw a couple of fights, in one of which the redoubtable Pancho was a competitor. He had by this time won the championship by defeating our own Jimmie Wilde. His reception was terrific; the natives went absolutely mad with enthusiasm. I have never seen an audience so alert to follow every move in a boxing ring. They were like so many needles and, their excitement communicating itself to the ordinary visitors, I found myself jumping and squirming about with every left-hook or upper-cut or solar-plexus punch delivered by the fighters. The Manila Stadium must have been built by a Londoner for it is an exact replica of the Ring, in Black-friars Road, London, only ten times larger. Every young Philippino wants to become a professional boxer. When Pancho Villa died the entire nation went into mourning.

I had hoped to spend a happy day or two with my old friend General Leonard Wood, the Governor General of the Islands, but his excellency had been called home on important business to Washington. However, he left me a letter of good-will, expressing the hope that Nance and I would enjoy ourselves in Manila and indicating some of the plans he had made for our entertainment before leaving. During the war days General Wood and I had made frequent appearances on public platforms in America and I formed a very high estimate of his character and cultured attainments. All the distinguished Americans and prominent Scots and Englishmen in the islands vied with each other in extending hospitality to my party. Mr. Kennedy, one of the leading bankers, gave a banquet in my honour and Mr. Scott, the managing director of a large firm of wood exporters, presented me with sufficient Philippine mahogany to make a parquet floor for my hall and study in Lauderdale, Dunoon. I may be wrong in describing this beautiful wood as mahogany but in any case it is very lovely, has a delightful odour which never quite disappears, and every time I walk across it at home my mind goes back to the glorious Philippine Islands and the many kind friends I have out there beneath the ever-blue sky of the sun-kissed Pacific.

CHAPTER TWENTY-FIVE

SOME FISH STORIES

I COMPLETED a fourteen months' tour by another extended visit to Australia, Tasmania, and New Zealand. This was the first time I had taken in Van Dieman's Land, as Tasmania used to be known in the old days, and the experience was novel and charming. Tasmania is a little England as the names of the territories, or counties, into which it is divided, at once suggest. There is a Devonshire, a Westmorland, a Dorset, a Cornwall, a Lincoln, and—so that Wales may not be left out altogether—there is a Montgomery and a Glamorgan! The island is rich in agriculture and sheep pastures and in the towns like Hobart, the capital, Launceston, and Burnie there are many thriving little industries. There is no poverty in Tasmania and no unemployment. The country is well governed by its own legislature and the governor is Sir James O'Grady a former Socialist Member of Parliament at Westminster and a most popular and able man. I have never in all my travels seen better roads than they have in Tasmania. They are little short of magnificent. I was told that they were built by convict labour in the days when Van Dieman's Land was a penal settlement for British malefactors; if this is so the convicts were amongst the world's best roadmakers and they have left behind them monuments that will last for centuries long after their murders, arsons, burglaries, sheepstealings, and highway robberies have been forgotten! I doff my Balmoral to the memory of these Tasmanian convicts and assert that they must have been splendid fellows. The population of the island is less than three hundred souls all told and I should think there must be room for hundreds of thousands more. But don't take this from me as authoritative

and start an international rush for Van Dieman's Land.
They may have all the people out there that they want! And
those they do have are certainly good!

When I reached New Zealand this time I was all on edge
to get amongst the trout in the rivers of the south island
once more. For over a year I had not had a rod in my hand.
All my life I have been an enthusiastic fisherman and if I
ever boast of anything it is in my ability to coax the finny
ones to my fly, minnow, or spinner. But whether I catch them
or not I yield to nobody—not even Bob Davis of New York
or Alec Mathewson of Dundee—in my passion for the past-
time immortalized by Isaac Walton. So those of my readers
who are anglers can well understand the delight with which
I looked forward to some trout fishing in New Zealand at
the end of a long and arduous tour.

Give me a rod and line and a Highland burn, or a Galloway loch, or a New Zealand river (all these, mark you, when
I cannot get to the Dee or the Don!) and I am the happiest
of mortals. I must have caught fish in more parts of the
world than most men whose fishing has been an adjunct to
hard work rather than a life's pursuit. While saying this, do
not imagine you are going to hear tales from me of giant
tarpon or tuna killed off the Florida coast, of sword fish
or sting rays weighing a thousand pounds, hooked in the
swarming waters down Panama Way. Some day when I can
afford the time—and the money!—I will get after these big
fellows and then I hope to write a book that will make
all anglers' mouths water.

In the meantime I am more than content to have an hour
or two with rod and line whenever I can fit it in with my
work. This summer, for instance, I have been several times
on Dupplin Loch, that angler's paradise on the estate of my
great friend Lord Forteviot. It is one of the best stocked
lochs in Scotland and the fish are rare fighters of splendid
size and quality. Many and many a basket have I filled at

Dupplin. Only last week I had nineteen fish, 22½ lbs., and if there are many better averages than this from a water more or less constantly fished I would sure like to hear of them. Lord Forteviot's keeper, John Crannie, is the most amazing fish expert I have ever met and the hours I have spent, either in his house or beside him in the boat, listening to his angling lore and philosophy have been altogether delightful to me. When I went up to Dupplin some time ago to open a new recreation hall in the model village over which Lord Forteviot reigns so benignly John was one of the audience and afterwards I asked him what he thought of my performance and the evening's revels generally. He scratched his head for a few seconds as if he were thinking out a reasoned criticism and then observed, "Sir Harry, there's been nothing like it in the country since Queen Victoria's funeral!"

One of the greatest thrills in a man's lifetime comes to him when he hooks his first salmon. I caught my first "fush" on the Dee many years ago now, and although I have landed many hundreds since that chilly May evening I have never again experienced the breath-catching joy which assails every sense as you realize that your fish is "on" and the music of the reel begins to sound in your ears. The "kill" I refer to happened on the stretch of the Dee owned by the late Mr. Duncan Davidson of Inchmarlo, near Banchory. He was a bonny fish of 25 lbs. and he fought me for fully twenty minutes. A "Jock Scott" did the trick; I have been partial to the illustrious Mr. Scott's fly from that day to this!

I have taken salmon from the Tay, the Deveron, the Spey, and the Tweed, and I have had splendid fishing on the Usk waters in South Wales owned by Lord Buckland, who, as Mr. Seymour Berry before he was raised to the British peerage, had so spectacular a career during and after the War. He is the oldest of three brothers who have all made their mark in British industry within a remarkably short time by the exercise of brilliant gifts as industrialists, finan-

Harry Lauder
on the —
"Minnihau" N.Z.

TROUT FISHING ON THE MINNEHAU, SOUTH ISLAND, NEW ZEALAND

ciers, and newspaper proprietors. Moreover they are thorough gentlemen and good sportsmen. Lord Buckland has a lovely home on the banks of the Usk, one of the best fishing rivers in Wales and I am looking forward to the time when I shall again whip a cast or two over his fine waters. There is grand fishing in Sutherlandshire, both river and loch, and the angler could not do better than spend a holiday on Loch Assynt or on wandering up and down the Inver or the Kirchaig. He will be sure to get lots of trout, as I have done on more than one occasion.

During my Indian tour the harbourmaster at Karachi gave me a real sporting day among the snappers twenty-five miles out at sea. We went out by tug. On the way to the fishing grounds the harbourmaster, an old Arbroath man, entertained me immensely by his disquisitions on fish and fishing in these Eastern waters. We caught a lot of fish that day of from two to twenty pounds in weight, mostly snappers. And, take my word for it, they are well named for they snap at the bait like hungry wolves. I ate a snapper on getting back to the hotel. It was very tasty indeed. I have also done a lot of deep-sea fishing off the coast of New South Wales where there seems to be a plenitude of all manner of fish. We caught so many different varieties that I cannot remember their names. But I do remember most distinctly the name of one big fellow I hooked—shark! He was five feet eight inches in length and weighed sixty-eight pounds. He fought like the sea-tiger he is and gave me as much excitement as I wanted. I landed another shark once off Hobart, the capital of Tasmania. This was a mammal and not a fish because when we got her aboard she disgorged six young ones from little pockets, like sausages. At Durban Harbour I have had good sport among the flat fish which appear to be the chief inhabitants of the seas round South Africa. They are of decent size but not very sporting from a fisherman's point of view.

I was almost on the point of saying that I had never had the chance of fishing while in the United States. Usually I have been so hard-worked there by Will Morris that I have had no time for angling and many a time I have gazed longingly at the American streams and rivers as we have flashed past them in the train. But I did once have an extraordinary fishing experience at Denver, of all places. Hearing from somebody that I was very fond of fishing, an admirer of mine in the Colorado city, Mr. Cliff Welch, invited me to have "as much fishing as I liked" on the private lake of a friend of his. This gentleman reared trout for sale to the hotels in Denver and did a very fair business. The lake was an artificial affair. It was perhaps a hundred yards long by fifty yards at its broadest point. There were reputed to be five thousand trout in it and they were fed daily with liver and light hash. All these facts I was unaware of before making my descent on the "preserved waters." When I arrived I found the lake frozen over. My disappointment was keen. But it was explained to me that this need not stop my fishing; one of the proprietor's servants got a big pole and smashed the ice all round the edges. So I started. My only trouble lay in seeing that my line did not foul the jagged ice anywhere and with this in view my "casting" was more like "poking" than the regulation action of a respectable angler. Did I catch any fish? I didn't *catch* them—it was pure murder. I had only one fly, a blue and black with a yellow body, but it did more execution than any single fly I have ever known. No sooner did it light on the water than a dozen trout came for it like bull-dogs. In spite of years of hand-feeding—more probably because of it—these trout were gluttons for the strange lure offered by my fly. I couldn't unhook them fast enough. In less than an hour I had forty or fifty pounders and pound-and-a-halfers lying on the icy bank of the lake. Then my conscience got the better of me. I stopped. It wasn't playing

the game and if I hadn't been desperate to have a rod in my
hand once more I could not have continued without bursting
into tears. When the owner of the lake came along to see
how I was faring among his speckled beauties, I had chucked
it. "Thank God, Sir Harry, you didn't fish any longer," he
remarked, "or you would have cleaned up the lake like a
thin-mesh net!" I have never told this story before. Any time
I have felt like telling it a wave of shame has swept over me
preventing the revelation of my one ghastly crime as a fisherman!

Next to Scotland the finest fishing country in the world
is undoubtedly New Zealand. I have fished all the rivers and
the lochs in South Island and have been rewarded with magnificent sport and overflowing baskets. My fishing cronies
down under are Donald MacDonald of Edendale, Invercargill, and Mr. John Smith, the proprietor of the Progressive
Stores in that purely Scottish town. We have had numerous
days together on the Matura, the Minnehau, the Wyndham,
and the New Rivers—all full of lovely trout of the Loch
Leven type and running from half a pound to four and five
and sometimes six pounds. The last time I was in New Zealand I sent home some photographs of my catches spread
out in front of me, or festooned behind me—you know the
usual type of fisherman's photograph. One of these I posted
to John Robertson, of Dundee, who fishes a stretch of the
Tay every year and in whose good company I have killed
many salmon, but all the acknowledgment I received from
him was a laconic post-card "Thanks for the fishing picture.
I don't believe it!"

There is a lake in the South Island called Te Anau in
which there exists a species of land-locked salmon. Fishermen will tell you that there can be no such thing; that the
salmon must get to the sea every year if it is to live. Well,
I am convinced that the "salmon" of Lake Te Anau *don't*

get to the sea. I have studied the configuration of the lake and the streams that run from it so closely that nothing will make me alter my opinion, namely, that the falls on these streams are so tremendous that they could not be "leaped" by any salmon that was ever spawned. Both MacDonald and Smith are always silent when I get on to this topic of the land-locked salmon of Te Anau. They are too orthodox fishermen to be otherwise than chary of giving a decided opinion either way—are they salmon or are they some other kind of fish closely resembling salmon? Here is a problem for anglers the world over to discuss. To me they look like salmon in every detail with the exception of girth—they don't seem to thicken. They are a beautiful silver fish with the flesh of salmon and the taste of a salmon. Game to a degree they fight for their lives with all the determination, the wiles, and the tenacity of a Tay fish. Curiously enough they will "take" neither fly nor spinner, only the minnow, and you have to be well up in the handling of this lure before they will respond readily to it. The general weight runs from three to eight pounds.

I trust my non-fishing readers will forgive me these rather lengthy digressions into purely piscatorial reminiscences but you all know how it is when fishermen start off—there's no stopping them. As a matter of fact I have gone back over many pages of fishing reflections and experiences and cut out a lot that I had originally intended to put in, fearing that I might bore those of you who are only interested in fish as a table food.

One final remark I would, however, like to make—and it is this. Would all the experts who agree with me that the fish of Lake Te Anau are land-locked salmon please write and say so. It would give me great joy, when I got to New Zealand next year for a long fishing holiday, to be armed with their opinions and pronouncements on a topic of supreme interest to fishermen everywhere. If they don't agree with me they needn't mind writing. And with that observation I think you have a very fair insight into the bigoted and "thrawn" (stubborn) mind of the average fisherman, myself included!

CHAPTER TWENTY-SIX

THE END OF THE ROAD

ONCE again I returned to America by the direct sea-route Sydney to San Francisco. When I first hit "Frisco" eighteen years ago it was an exceedingly hot spot on the then rather hectic Barbary Coast. There were sights and "doin's" in the old town that would not be tolerated today; even Chicago had nothing on the great western seaport for excitement, sensation, and general lawlessness. But within recent years it has quietened down to an eminent respectability, thanks in great measure, I should say, to the wise, popular and progressive rule of my friend Mayor Rolph. For something like sixteen years now Mr. Rolph has adorned the civic chair of the city; the inhabitants refuse to give him up and thereby show their good taste and common-sense. Rolph and I are good friends and I get a most genial welcome from him every time I arrive at 'Frisco either by sea or railroad. Tom asserts that the Mayor is one of the very best men in the world but I have a suspicion that Thomas is prejudiced in his favour on account of the fact that the Mayor entertained him and his wife at a banquet in honour of their silver wedding.

Seeing that I am back again in the States I may as well take the opportunity—I shall not have another in these memoirs—to recall several of the more amusing experiences and incidents of my twenty years touring of a country which, to my mind—and quite apart from certain obvious reasons— never loses its interest and fascination. Only the fact that I am getting older and thus not so keen on seeing new places and new faces prevents me from bubbling over with enthusiasm at the start of each new American "attack" by

the Lauder-Morris combination of gold-diggers. But in
the old days it was different. I was constantly breaking new
ground. Every year I was up against fresh propositions and
with no certainty that they would pan out successfully.
There were whole vast tracts of the American continent
where the name of Harry Lauder was unknown.

Take the case of the theatre-proprietor in Peoria, Illinois.
When our advance man went up there to book the theatre
for a matineé performance he found the German owner very
unwilling to come to any arrangement without a sum down
as a guarantee. He had been left in the cart so often, he
explained, by these new guys with a New York reputation
only. The advance man laughed his fears to scorn and said
that "Harry Lauder was the greatest thing that has struck
the American continent since Columbus." This line of tall
talk settled the doubts of the German proprietor who didn't
like to admit that he had never heard of Columbus, and
sharing terms were fixed up forthwith. Just as our man was
leaving the theatre the proprietor turned to him and remarked, "Say, young feller, you ain't never told me the
name of the chap this Lauder guy's gonna fight!"

Tom himself went down from Richmond, Virginia, to
fix up a flying matinée at a little town forty or fifty miles
away. The arrangements were completed satisfactorily and
Tom thought he might as well give the dressing-rooms the
once over. He found the accommodation consisted of one
large room underneath the stage. "But what about the lady
artistes?" asked Tom. "You know we have several women
performers—how do you keep them apart from the gentlemen?" "Apart?" said the other in a puzzled way. "Why—
don't they speak? Are they not friends?" It was at Richmond, by the way, that I laughed consumedly at a notice
stuck up near the stage-door. It read "To Artistes—Don't
send out your washing until the management sees your act!"
At a theatre in Rochester, New York, I saw posted up above

the mail rack this frank notice—"If there's no mail here for you don't ask—you have been forgotten by everybody who ever knew you!"

When I first went to Butte, Montana, the principal means of transport from the station to the town, about a mile away, was an old cab driven by an aged negro. There may have been other vehicles but at all events this aged Jehu drove us both to and from the town. On the return journey I asked him irritably why it was they had built the station so far from the town. "I don't jes' know, boss," he replied, "unless it was to have depot near railroad!" And if you can beat that as a smart answer to a stupid question you have my full permission!

The last time I was in Butte, a year or two ago, the weather was so intensely cold that the engine of our special train froze up and we were delayed half a day. Several members of the orchestra were assembled in the lounge of the hotel and one of their number remembered that he had a friend in the town who was more than likely to have a bottle or two of whisky in his house. A collection was made on the spot and, armed with ten or twelve dollars, the musician in question set out on his mission of mercy. He was gone for about an hour and then returned, his face wreathed in smiles, and gripping to his bosom a brown paper parcel in the unmistakable shape of a bottle. There was an immediate rush for the returned missionary and one of his enraptured colleagues slapped him so heavily on the back that the parcel fell to the floor and was smashed into smithereens. Two of the orchestra got severely injured in the ensuing mêlée and three others had their tongues, lips, and noses badly cut by broken glass!

Nine-tenths of all the stories in America today deal, of course, with Prohibition. The Ford joke is dead—killed by the bootleggers. I always say myself that Prohibition is almost as bad as not being able to get a drink! And this

ON THE BEACH AT ATLANTIC CITY

reminds me of a laughable incident which occurred in my
dressing-room last year at Washington, D. C. A certain well-
known Congressman (you couldn't get his name from me
if you paid me a dollar!) came round to have a chat and
from his hip pocket he produced what we would call in
Glasgow a half-mutchkin. There were no glasses in the
room but I had two paper tumblers and into these he poured
the contents of his flask. Just as we were about to say
"Here's how!" there was a knock at the door and another
visitor came in, but not before we had concealed the tumblers
behind a looking-glass. You see we didn't want to tantalize
the newcomer and, moreover, we didn't feel like sharing the
"blessing" with him. So we waited until he went away and
then jointly dashed for the "hidie-hole." To our united
horror we found that the paper tumblers had absorbed all
the whisky—in fact they were practically eaten away! There
they lay, wilted, drunken and repulsive objects!

At Sweetgrass on the Alberta-Dakota border our train
was boarded one night by the U. S. prohibition officers. Tom,
I believe, had instructed all the members of our company to
come right across with the truth about any liquor they might
have in their trunks or hand-bags. They all did so with the
exception of the trombone player who swore he had nothing
at all to declare. On leaving the train the chief officer called
Tom aside and remarked, "That guy in lower-eight berth
had four bottles of hooch beneath his bed. Now he ain't got
any. I've got two and you'll find a couple in your small grip.
See an' stick to 'em. Honesty's the best policy!"

Musicians as a class are the most extraordinary men you
can meet with anywhere. I always say that every musician
is a genius and it is an accepted axiom that genius is akin
to madness. We had one fellow travel with us who manufactured his own gin. How he did it nobody ever found out but
when we were in a place for any length of time he used to
lock himself up in his room for hours on end. Sometimes

he was successful in his efforts as a private distiller and sometimes he was not. But we always knew when he had "done the trick" because he started chasing himself all over the hotel or the theatre; he doped himself with his own devil's brew until he was mad as a March hare. He disappeared during one of his outbursts and we never saw him again.

Another musician in our travelling orchestra—and many of these chaps made tour after tour with the Lauder vaudeville parties—had a wholesale dread of rats and mice. Wherever he went, theatre, hotel, restaurant, train, or boat, the first question he asked was, "Any rats or mice about here?" The other boys were not slow to take advantage of his horror of these vermin and many a laugh and joke they had at his expense. But the best "lark" of all in this connection was quite unpremeditated and had originally nothing whatever to do with the fellow who hated rats and mice. Only he got mixed up in the joke as you shall see. The leader of our orchestra was a charming man whom I will call Jack Blunt and who had two outstanding characteristics—he wore a toupee and made a practice of having forty winks in the band-room every night before the show commenced. He was a practical joker himself and was very fond of stringing Tom when he got the chance, which wasn't often. So Tom determined to have his revenge. Going into the band-room one evening while Jack was asleep he tied the end of a length of black linen thread to the toupee and arranged with the drummer to hand up the other end to him, standing in the wings, after Jack had taken his place at the leader's seat. Thomas didn't dare "pull anything" while I was on the stage but waited for the next turn to mine, which was a diabolo act by the greatest expert in this line I have ever seen —Jack Ark. Ark was in the middle of his fancy work, and "Blunt" was putting in an equally fancy obligato to the performance when the latter felt his toupee suddenly jerked

off his head. He immediately let bow and fiddle fall to the
ground and put up his hands to discover what had happened
to his thatch. Almost at the same moment the viola player
two rows behind—the man who hated rats—saw something
furry scurry between his legs. Bounding up from his chair
with a wild shriek he seized his viola by the neck and
brought it down, crash! on what he thought to be a member
of the loathsome tribe of rodents. Instantly the theatre was
in an uproar. The diabolist bolted off the stage; the other
musicians stopped playing to let their merriment have full
sway, while the audience, completely puzzled by the commotion in the band-pit, rose to their feet in alarm and many
of them hurried from the theatre under the impression that
several of the orchestra had all at once gone mad! Tom
himself was rather upset at the too complete success of his
practical joke.

At Denver one evening the demand for admission was
so heavy that the management arranged some dozens of
seats round the stage. The seat nearest the orchestra on
the prompt side was occupied by an elderly gentleman with
a long beard and a pair of chilly blue eyes and I could not
help noticing that he never allowed his stern features to
relax for an instant. All my patter, jokes and prancings
around left him stone cold. So when I came to sing "A Wee
Deoch-an-Doris" I determined to have one smile out of the
guy even if I had to throw a double somersault or bat the
conductor one on the bean with my crooked stick. An idea
occurred to me—why not get him to join in the chorus? So
at the end of the opening verse I went over to him, first
holding up my hand to the audience for silence, and genially
remarked, "Now, father, throw oot yer chest and join me
in this chorus!" The old man got up from his seat, poked
a threatening forefinger in my face and observed in a high-
pitched voice audible all over the theatre, "See, here, Lauder,
I ain't none o' yer bloody chorus—I paid for my seat up

here. Get on with yer own job yourself!" My palpable
amazement at the old man's gall made the house rock with
amusement and the laughter was renewed when he rose
from his seat and stalked off the stage in high dudgeon.

This incident reminds me of another which took place
in a little fit-up theatre in a small mining town in Western
Australia. The limes were being very badly managed by the
operator in the fly and Tom was hissing instructions, mingled
with maledictions, to the unseen personage who was constantly missing the vital "spot." At last Tom could stand it
no longer, and, with an oath, cried up, "Heavens, man, can't
you do what I'm telling you?" Suddenly a head shot out
over the fly-gallery into the full view of the audience and a
shrill voice exclaimed, "I'm not a man, I'm a woman, and
if you speak like that to me again I'll come down and knock
you clean into the middle of next week, damn you!" This
entirely unrehearsed interlude was much to the liking of the
audience and the belligerent lime-light lady came in for a
hearty round of applause.

I am often asked to say what is the funniest thing I
have ever seen in the course of my world-wide wanderings.
And I really think the palm must be given to an entertainment I saw one evening at the Sharkey Club in New York.
Dominic Buckley took me along there many years ago when
one of the items of entertainment was a fight between six
niggers. I had never seen anything like this before and
didn't think it could possibly be either edifying or amusing.
The former, let me admit at once, it certainly was not! But
amusing—I laughed until the tears rolled down my cheeks!
Not until that night did I thoroughly understand the significance of the phrase—sore with laughing. It was not a case
of two-and-two or three-and-three; it was each against all
and all against each. Just try to imagine the scene from the
gong. You'll have to imagine it because I cannot hope to
describe it. But in a general way I must try. Six nervous,

wary, but tremendously keen niggers suddenly leave the ropes to indulge in a general mix-up. They have no settled plan of action and it would be of no use to them if they had. They have no idea what is coming to them—or from what quarter—all they know is that they have to hit wherever, and whoever, they happen to come up against. This they start in to do with commendable energy and rapidity. Two of them, let us say, commence a nice little argument of their own and are getting along famously with it when an unexpected punch from some outside agency alters the whole course of events. Enraged beyond measure at this impertinent interference with their individual battle the original couple will turn together on the newcomer and only the advent of another stray wallop, or sudden upper-cut, will prevent him being "outed" on the spot. The black ingredients of this fistic "pudding" get all stirred up together in the most laughable way; the fray ranges from end to end, corner to corner, of the ring in amazing and kaleidoscopic fashion. There is absolutely no "fear or favour, affection or ill-will," as the Scottish lawyers have it—the six combatants slug, drive, hook, swing, jolt, upper-cut or kidney-punch with complete freedom and entire lack of prejudice. One of the black fellows may side-step a murderous blow from the right only to meet an equally devastating attack from the left. A daring frontal effort by another may have all the sting taken from it by a sudden pile-driver from the rear. If there are one or two big chaps in the sextette it is more than probable that they will early have been signalled out for general punishment and that before the conflict has proceeded many minutes these same big chaps are heartily glad to crawl for their lives beneath the ropes.

Gradually the original six is reduced to five and then four and then two, for all the world like the six little piggies that went to market. The night I was at the Sharkey Club the battle resulted in a draw between two most valiant niggers who were so exhausted that when they finally reeled up against each other they fell to the floor in a heap—and went to sleep on the spot. Entertainments of this kind are not now allowed in America and, on the whole, I think the authorities are quite right! But I still laugh every time I think about the black mélange at the old Sharkey Club with my good pal Dominic Buckley.

Tom Vallance is one of the best fellows in the world as a rule but he has a wicked temper at times, as I myself have good reason to know. At Toronto on one occasion all our company had to be vaccinated on account of a smallpox scare. Tom had the doctor aside and told him that he had been vaccinated only a year previously. But the doctor shook his head. "I get a dollar a head for this job and every one o' you birds has to earn me a buck. There are forty o' you all told and I got forty dopes—no more an' no less. I aint takin' none back with me!" "Oh," said Tom, "if that's all your grouch you can give my share to the drummer—he an' I are not on speaking terms!" To this monstrous suggestion the medical man agreed with a nod and a wink. And the innocent drummer was off duty for a fortnight! I only heard the story a week later and I wasn't feeling so good myself that I could take the trouble to dress Tom down.

Once we had to wait until three o'clock in the morning to catch a train out of Chicago for a town in Indiana. Most of us went to an all-night picture show to pass the time. The second picture thrown on the screen was a war-time scenario supposed to have been taken in Germany and the main incident in which was the actual declaration of war by the German cabinet. A very snappy scene depicted the Kaiser slowly and dramatically getting to his feet, raising his hand and announcing, per title, "I Declare For War, Gentlemen!" We had with us at the time a little Italian piccolo-player who had just returned nursing some nasty wounds, from serving as a soldier on the Piave. He was seated about four places

from me in the row immediately behind. When he saw the
Kaiser make his melodramatic pronouncement his emotions
got the better of him and, whipping out a pistol, he fired
point-blank at the Kaiser's head. The audience ducked as
one man and hundreds started a scramble on all fours for
the nearest exits. Even in Chicago they don't like their pictures interlarded with actual gun-play. The place was
instantly in a commotion. A "cuppla bulls" enjoying the show
near the Italian pounced upon him and lugged him off to
the station. He was fined twenty-five dollars and told by the
magistrate that he was "damned lucky not to have shot the
President of the United States!"

And now I must face the difficult task of drawing these
Roamin's in the Gloamin' of my life to a close. When I was
a wee boy attending church every Sunday in Arbroath I used
to think the Minister's "Lastly, my brethren" the most wea-
risome part of the whole service. How I wished he would
hurry up and get it over. My readers who have followed me
thus far might feel the same way about my final paragraphs.
From a stage point of view an exit is much more important
than an entrance and personally I have always tried to leave
the stage with the audience wanting just a little bit more. I
have an idea that it should be the same way now. Yet how am
I to plan it? I am about to say farewell to the greatest and
most critical audience before which I have ever appeared in
my life and I am anxious not to make a mistake. Because
there will be no "next show" to provide me with an opportunity of rectifying my error. In this respect I am like the
Aberdeen man who was walking down Union Street in company with the only Jew who ever managed to earn a living
in the northern capital of Scotland. All at once the Jew bent
down and picked up half-a-crown from the pavement in front
of the Aberdonian's feet. The latter said nothing—but hurried off to have his eyesight tested at an oculist's. After-

wards he explained to his friends that he couldn't afford to make the same mistake twice!

So, rehearsals in leave-taking being out of the question, how shall I end these memories and stories of a career which often astonishes me when I fall into reflective mood at "ma ain fireside," in my bed, in the train or on the ocean liner, at home or abroad? Perhaps I may be able to convey something of what is in my mind if I say that, had I to live my life all over again, there is really little in it from a purely personal standpoint that I would like to alter. God knows the difference it would have made to me had my only boy been spared from the ravages of war, but the mysterious workings of Providence ought not to be taken into consideration when a man is weighing up his own life and actions. All such regrets and longings put aside, however, I cannot see where I would have had the course of my life changed in any way. Certainly not the early poverty and hardships, the bitter fight for bread as a mill-boy and a miner; certainly not the dawning ambitions and the determined strivings after their attainment; most assuredly not the years of clash, clamour and conflict, with their gradual building up of what people call "fame and fortune." No, these are the real things in any man's life—up to a point. They are the things truly worth living and fighting for—up to a point. Then comes the point. And it is here that every man must answer certain questions for himself. There is no compulsion upon me publicly to answer all the questions that occasionally arise in my own mind and I do not propose to do so.

But one or two of them I shall not hesitate to discuss. Perhaps I ask myself if I have always been scrupulously honest and straightforward in my dealings with my fellow-men, if my word has been as good as my bond, if I have ever let a friend down, if I have ever owed one penny-piece, if I have in all my life wilfully done an unkind or a cruel act—and I tell myself that my conscience is clear on all these things. Have I forgiven much of insult, approbrium, of injustice, of false report, of malicious lies, of many thousands of pounds lent and never returned and I reply—yes, freely. Have I raised by my own efforts and downright hard work great funds for war and charitable purposes all over the world, and again I say to myself—"Yes, Harry, that is so." Am I entitled to all the money I have earned? Surely I am as much entitled to it as the managers and proprietors who made thousands and thousands off me when they were paying me a hundredth part of what I was worth to them? In any case (I argue to myself) the Socialists can have no possible quarrel with me for I never compelled people to pay to hear me; all that I have today has been a free-will offering on the altar of any talent I may possess or any pleasure I may have been able to bestow.

But have I done all that I might have done? Have any of us done all that we might have done? Have I been as sympathetic, as gracious, as kindly, as ready to open my purse to all-comers as a man of my income ought to be, according to popular belief? Have I not hardened my heart to the needs and the claims of others just a bit too much? Have I carried the totally undeserved reputation for Scottish "carefulness" to a line bordering on the excessive? Have I failed to realize, in fact, that money was "made to go round"? Well, perhaps I have. But will you let me make a confession? Money, purely as money, has meant very little indeed to me all my life. My wants are small; they have always been small and will continue to be small. It's the fighting for it that has intrigued me, the pulling of it "into the house," the knowledge that white, black, brown, and yellow men have been willing to pay it out to hear me and see me and cheer me! And, after that, the cosy feeling that there's enough in the bank for all eventualities is not to be sneezed at! There I am—joking when I really meant to be serious.

What remains to be said? Very little, I think. I am not going to retire yet a while; I would only be miserable if I had no work to do and at the moment Will Morris and I are planning still another farewell tour of America. After that I shall settle down at Dunoon for a bit and then, perhaps about 1929, make a long summer trip to all the Scottish towns in which I established the basis of my reputation thirty years ago. This is a project I have long had in mind and already I am looking forward to it with great joy and keen anticipation for the memories it will revive. Still plotting and planning—you will say. I cannot help it. It's in my blood and will, I suppose, be there right on till the End of the Road.

Keep right on to the end of the road
Keep right on to the end.
If the way be rough let your heart be strong
Keep right on round the bend.
Though you're tired and weary still journey on
Till you come to that happy abode
Where all you've loved and been longing for
Will be there—at the End of the Road!

THE END